PHOTO-ATLAS
of the
UNITED STATES

A Complete Photographic Atlas of
The U.S.A. Using Satellite Photography

WARD RITCHIE PRESS

PASADENA, CALIFORNIA

Produced by
Photo-Geographic International
Mt. View, California

Executive Producer
James R. Grady

Director of Composition
Joan C. Soasey

Contributing Geographers:
David E. Schwarz
Dr. Floyd M. Henderson
Michael A. Romanov

Staff Cartographers:
Gail Holland Thelin
John Hickey
Deborah Walker Schwarz

Geological Consultant
Richard A. Smith

Cartographic Artists:
Marie F. Grady
Jack Wible

Chicago

This photo-map shows evidence of Chicago's importance in transportation. Highways and railroads gathered from the entire nation can be seen to converge on **"The Loop"**—Chicago's central business district. **O'Hare International Airport,** toward the upper left of the photo-map, is the world's busiest commercial airport, although **Midway Field** (appropriately in the center of the picture) remains an important center of transport.

Since the opening of the St. Lawrence Seaway in 1959, large ocean-going ships can be seen docked at **Chicago** ports even though the city is some 700 miles from the ocean. Chicago also became the link between barge traffic on the Mississippi River system and the Great Lakes when canals were dredged through the former narrow portage which separated them.

The development of clouds can be seen in the lower right. Scientists have observed unusually heavy rainfall over northwestern **Indiana** during the last few decades and some attribute this to the increased amount of particulate matter introduced into the atmosphere by steel mills, autos and other pollution sources in the Chicago area. Condensation of moisture around these particles would be expected to fall as rain somewhat downwind (usually eastward) of the city.

Stretching for over a hundred miles to the south and west of **Chicago** is some of the flattest and perhaps the richest cropland in the world. This area, smoothed and enriched thousands of years ago by gigantic sheets of ice, can be seen to have yielded readily to the regular square pattern of the U.S. Public Land Survey because of its flatness.

Introduction

This is the first atlas showing complete photographic coverage of the United States. The photography has recently been made available by space programs such as Landsat and Skylab. Photographing the entire country is almost impossible without the use of satellites. Aircraft fly too low to photograph very large areas and, at any given time, some portion of the United States is covered by clouds. Only a continuously orbiting satellite such as Landsat could accomplish the task.

The photo-maps in this Photo-Atlas are composed of pictures from Landsat, Skylab, and high-altitude aircraft such as the U-2 and the RB57. There are two basic types of photo-maps that make up the atlas. The earth-blue duotone photo-maps give complete coverage of the United States and the full-color photo-maps show enlarged, detailed coverage of major cities. The earth-blue duotone photo-maps are photo mosaics of Landsat imagery* while the full-color photo-maps are composed of photos from Skylab or high-altitude aircraft. More than 600 individual Landsat images (about 7 inches square) have been photo-mosaiced together forming 60 photo-maps covering the 48 conterminous states plus Alaska. (Hawaii is shown in a color Skylab photo.) The photography used in this photo-atlas is available to the public from the Earth Resources Observation System (EROS) Data Center at Sioux Falls, South Dakota. Landsat mosaics are available from the Soil Conservation Service Cartographic Division in Hyattsville, Maryland.

Photo-maps are in many ways superior to ordinary maps. Mountains, rivers, valleys, and lakes are shown in their exact shapes and relative sizes on photo-maps. The accuracy of ordinary maps is limited by the ability of the cartographic artist. Mountains and valleys on ordinary maps are usually shown with exaggerated relief. On photo-maps the relief is exact and any shadows are shown to exact proportions. Agriculture and other man-made patterns on the land are also shown in exact detail, including urban sprawl (e.g., the Dallas-Fort Worth area on photo-map pp. 82-83) and the scars of strip mining (e.g., photo-map pp. 98-99).

Neither ordinary maps nor photo-maps can show the true color of the landscape because of seasonal effects on vegetation. Ordinary maps use color primarily to show elevation, but it is often wrongly interpreted as vegetation. The color photo-maps in this Photo-Atlas have been produced via an exclusive process to depict the actual color of the landscape on a clear, spring day.

The duotone photo-maps that make up the bulk of this atlas show features on the land at a scale of 18 miles to the inch. The standard photo-map in this photo-atlas, a two page spread, shows an area of land approximately 280 miles wide by 210 miles long.

The Photo-Atlas makes an ideal guide for airline passengers looking out the aircraft window. The average land speed of an airliner is 600 miles per hour. The airliner will fly over the length of a photo-map in about 29 minutes.

The shadows in all of the earth-blue photo-maps are cast toward the northwest. The two Landsat satellites orbit the Earth in a ''sun-synchronous'' path that keeps them slightly ahead of the sun. This insures that all Landsat imagery will be lighted by approximately the same late morning sun and all shadows will be in the same direction. True north orientation is the top of each photo-map.

Words in bold print are named or directly pointed out on the photo-map. It is impossible to describe or even name every detail on the photo-maps. If every city and town were named, as is the case with an ordinary road map, the entire photograph would be covered with printing, making it impossible to view the landscape. Instead, the cities and towns named on the photo-maps have been selected with the intention of helping the reader locate features on the land. The descriptive paragraphs are limited to the outstanding visual features considered important by geographers, geologists, and historians.

James Grady
Photo Geographic International

Acknowledgments:

U.S. Geological Survey
Earth Resources Observation
  Systems
(EROS) Data Center,
Sioux Falls, South Dakota

Department of Geography and
Department of Natural Science
at San Jose State University,
San Jose, California.

U.S. Department of Agriculture,
Soil Conservation Service,
Cartographic Division,
Hyattsville, Maryland.

U.S. Geological Survey,
Western Region Headquarters,
Menlo Park, California.

Dr. Burton L. Gordon,
Department of Geography,
San Francisco State University,
San Francisco, California.

Satellite Data Library,
The University of Wisconsin,
Madison, Wisconsin.

The National Aeronautics and
Space Administration,
Ames Research Center,
Moffet Field, California

Forestry Remote Sensing
  Laboratory
University of California,
Berkeley, California

The United States Air Force

* The words ''imagery'' and ''photography'' are synonomous (both words are defined in dictionaries as a picture, or a recording of light) and are so used in this atlas. This is contrary to some esoteric, technical uses where imagery and photography refer to the indirect and direct recording of light, respectively.

AP

The only rain forests in the United States are located on the **Olympic Peninsula** along the western slopes of the **Olympic Mountains.** These forests receive over 150 inches of rainfall annually. Vegetation growth is dense and luxurient. Century-old trees grow to heights of over 300 feet.

The coastal mountain ranges of Washington and Oregon capture much of the moisture brought in from the sea. The precipitation rate results in the growth of large forests with Douglas Fir as the predominant tree.

The light speckled areas among the peaks of the **Cascade Range** result from the logging practice of clear cutting, where every tree in an area is cut. The unuseable ones are left where they fall. Hopefully, the forest can regenerate itself to provide another crop of trees.

Puget Sound, a great embayment with hundreds of islands, is part of a long trough extending from Oregon to Alaska between the Pacific mountain ranges. The Sound has several deep, natural harbors which have fostered the growth of cities like **Seattle, Tacoma** and **Everett.**

The **Cascade Range** is an uplifted block topped by volcanoes and lava flows. **Mt. Rainier** (14,408 ft.) is one of the volcanoes which appear on this photo-map. In 1969, **Mt. Rainier** became geologically active and began to warm up slightly. Geologists expressed some concern that a continued warming trend could cause melting of Rainier's 28 glaciers.

During the last Ice Age, a glacier blocked the present course of the **Columbia River** at the site of the **Grand Coulee Dam,** forcing the river to cut a new channel to the south. When the glacier retreated, the river resumed its normal course but left behind a high, deep channel (a coulee). Engineers made use of the dried up bed of the **Grand Coulee** to create **Banks Lake,** an equalizing reservoir. The **Grand Coulee Dam** is one of the largest concrete structures on earth. It provides electric power and over 5,000 miles of irrigation canals to the Columbia Basin and the Pacific Northwest.

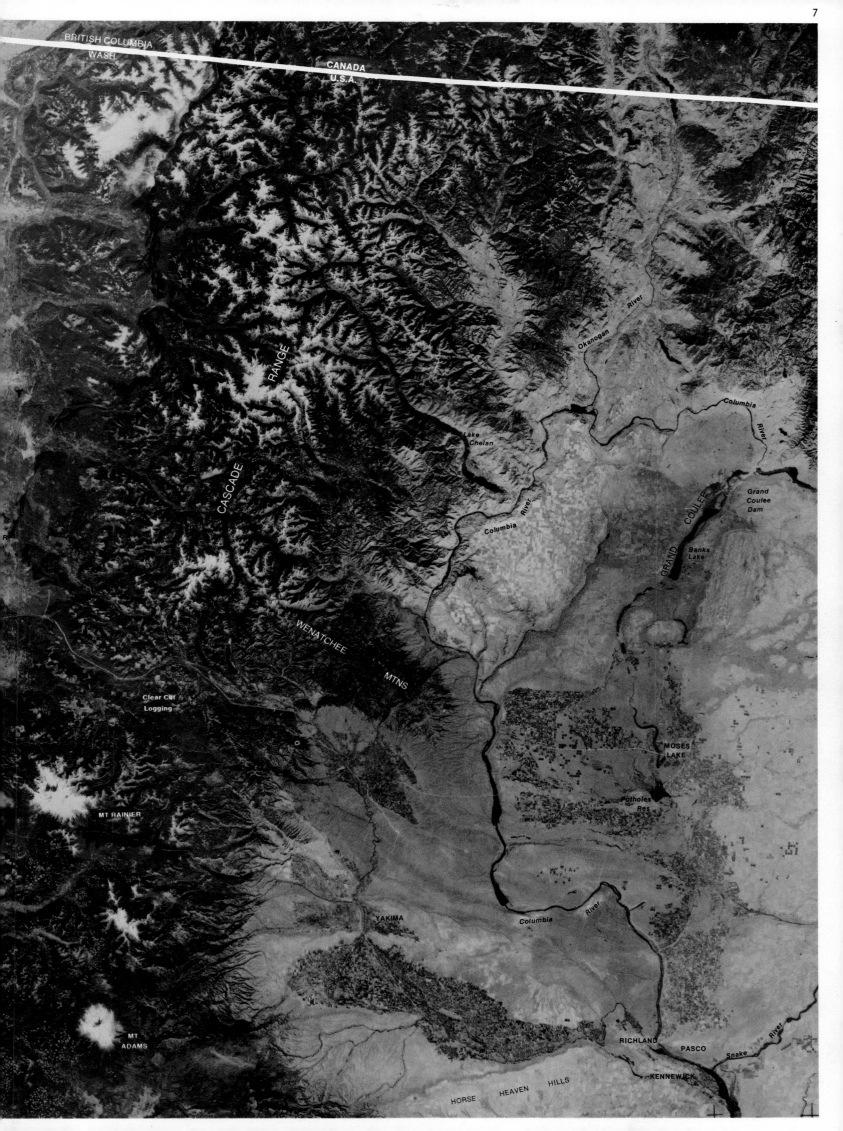

BRITISH COLUMBIA
WASH

CANADA
U.S.A.

RANGE

CASCADE

Okanogan

River

Columbia

River

Lake
Chelan

Columbia

River

GRAND

COULEE

Grand
Coulee
Dam

Banks
Lake

WENATCHEE

MTNS

Clear Cut
Logging

MOSES
LAKE

Potholes
Res

MT RAINIER

YAKIMA

Columbia

River

MT
ADAMS

RICHLAND

PASCO

Snake

River

KENNEWICK

HORSE HEAVEN HILLS

Once a raging, wild river, representing the last precarious leg of the Oregon Trail, the **Columbia** is now tamed by a series of dams supplying hydro-electric power and irrigation. The artificial lakes created by these dams are visible on this photo-map. The **Columbia River,** draining 250,000 square miles, contains one third of America's total potential water energy.

Mountains **Hood, Adams, Jefferson,** and the **Three Sisters** form part of the "spine" of the **Cascade Range.** The **Cascades** extend into Northern California and merge into the **Sierra Nevada.**

Oregon's **Willamette River Valley,** located between the **Coast Range** and the **Cascade Range,** supports diversified agriculture.

Between **Florence** and **Coos Bay,** Oregon's "shifting" sand dunes can be seen. Slowly moved by the wind, they have engulfed trees, homes, and roads.

Crater Lake was created about 7,000 years ago by the volcanic destruction of Mount Mazama, then the tallest mountain in the world. With a depth of 1,932 feet, it is the deepest lake in the United States. The small cone island visible in the western half of the lake is Wizard Island, which juts 763 feet above the water.

Much of southeastern Oregon is desert. The **Great Sandy Desert,** southeast of **Bend,** and the **Harney Basin** receive less than 8 inches of rainfall annually.

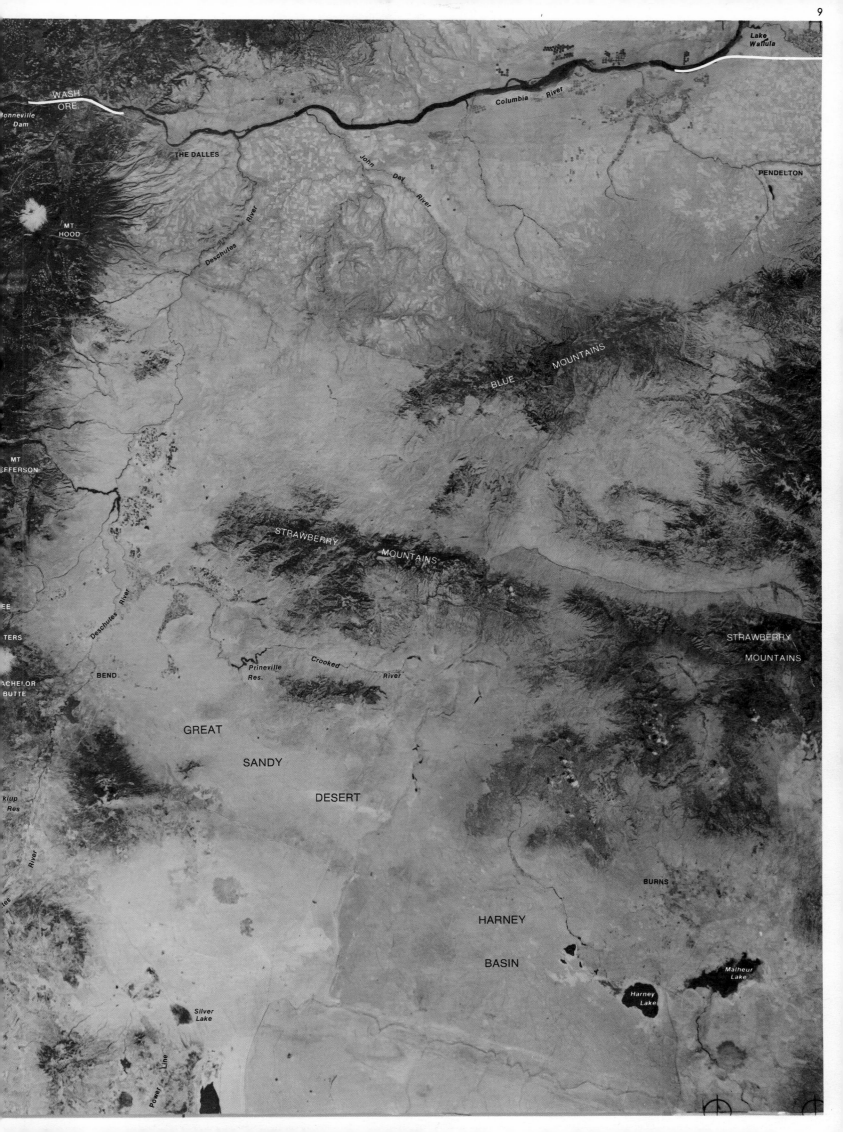

WASH
ORE.

Bonneville
Dam

THE DALLES

MT
HOOD

Columbia River

John Day River

Deschutes River

PENDELTON

BLUE MOUNTAINS

MT
JEFFERSON

STRAWBERRY

MOUNTAINS

Deschutes River

EE

TERS

ACHELOR
BUTTE

BEND

Prineville
Res.

Crooked River

STRAWBERRY

MOUNTAINS

GREAT

SANDY

DESERT

BURNS

kiup
Res

HARNEY

River

BASIN

Malheur
Lake

Harney
Lake

Silver
Lake

tes

Power Line

Lake
Wallula

The mountainous regions on this photo-map are home territory for "Sasquatch" (Bigfoot). The existence of these 9-foot-tall, hairy, man-like creatures is controversial, but sightings are frequently reported by fishermen, hunters, lumbermen, and Indians native to the area.

Upper Klamath Lake, Clear Lake, Tule Lake and **Lower Klamath Lake** are national wildlife refuges for millions of geese and ducks migrating the Pacific "flyway". These Klamath Basin refuges have the largest seasonal concentration of waterfowl in North America.

There are at least 120 volcanic peaks in the southern **Cascades.** The most prominent is **Mount Shasta,** rising 2 miles above the land at its base. Southeast of **Mount Shasta** is **Lassen Peak** which erupted in 1914 and 1915, lifting vapor and ashes to heights of 40,000 feet. Lava flows, obstructing valleys, formed several small lakes and meadows near the mountain. The region contains many hot springs and fumaroles.

The completion of **Shasta Dam** in 1944 provided the first major water storage unit in the Central Valley Project—a project to regulate the flow of the **Sacramento River** and provide irrigation storage, flood control, and hydroelectricity to the **Sacramento Valley.**

Shasta Lake, the finger-like reservoir created by the dam, has over 365 miles of shoreline and is a major recreational area.

The redwood forest belt extends along the coastline the entire length of this photo-map.

Pyramid Lake is supplied with water from Lake Tahoe (see photo-map pp. 12-13) via the **Truckee River.** The lake is named after the pyramid-shaped island near the east bank.

Pyramid Lake, Walker Lake, and **Carson Lake** (see photo-map pp. 12-13) are shrunken remnants of ancient Lake Lahontan. During the ice ages, this lake covered more than 8,000 square miles along the eastern base of the **Sierra Nevada.**

KLAMATH
FALLS

Lake
Albert

Hart
Lake

Crump
Lake

Lower
Klamath
Lake

Tule
Lake

Clear Lake
Res.

Goose
Lake

ORE.
NEV.

Upper
Lake

CALICO   MOUNTAINS

Power Line

Pit   River

Middle
Alkali
Lake

Lower
Lake

DESERT

BLACK   ROCK

Eagle
Lake

CALIF.
NEV.

MT LASSEN

Mt. Meadows
Res.

Lake
Almanor

Honey
Lake

SIERRA

Pyramid
Lake

NEVADA

Feather   River

The **Marysville Buttes** rise over 2,000 feet from the **Sacramento Valley** floor. This circular area of volcanic domes contrasts sharply with the surrounding agricultural land.

Lake Tahoe was formed about 1 million years ago during a separation of the eastern **Sierras.** Because of its depth (1,645 feet), the lake never freezes over.

In the foothills of the Sierras, east of **Sacramento,** is the historic Mother Lode region. Gold discovered here attracted the 49'ers, causing a sudden growth in the population of northern California.

Giant redwood trees cover the seaward slopes of the **Santa Cruz** Mountains. The western slopes of all the coast ranges are rich in vegetation—receiving the bulk of the water carried by winds from the Pacific Ocean.

It is possible to trace the **San Andreas Fault** along the west side of the **Diablo Range** northward through the San Francisco Peninsula. The land west of this fault moves to the north during earthquakes.

The vegetation on the west slope of the **Sierra Nevada** changes with elevation:

| Grass-land | Chaparral and Oaks | Conifers (ponderosa pines) |

1000' Valley   Foothills   10,000' Sierra Nevada

The **Sierra Nevada** Range is essentially one block of granite 350 miles long and 60 miles wide which has been tipped upward. The western slopes are gentle with many deep valleys such as the **Yosemite.**

Between the **coast ranges** and the **Sierra Nevada** lies the great Central Valley of California. Using irrigation, this 400-mile-long valley is the agricultural heart of California—the number one agricultural state. A tremendous variety of crops are grown, ranging from rice and olives in the north to cotton and citrus fruits in the south.

The **California Aqueduct** runs along the western edge of the **San Joaquin Valley** (the southern half of the Central Valley) carrying water from the Sacramento River for agriculture and for the heavily populated southland.

Lake Oroville

Folsom Lake

AMENTO

SIERRA

NEVADA

Mokelumne River

Camanche Res.

STOCKTON

San

Stanislaus River

Joaquin River

Tuolomne River

Don Pedro Res

Merced River

SAN

San Luis Res

LOS BANOS

JOAQUIN

VALLEY

FRESNO

Milerton Lake

Pine Flat Res

San Joaquin River

SIERRA

Lake Crowley

NEVADA

YOSEMITE

NATIONAL

PARK

Mono Lake

BODIE

East Walker River

Walker

West Walker River

Walker Lake

WASSUK RANGE

Walker River

Carson River

Carson Lake

CARSON CITY

Washoe Lake

Lake Tahoe

RENO

Truckee River

The beautiful Big Sur coast (Sur is Spanish for south) begins at **Point Sur** and stretches southward for over 50 miles. Steep cliffs, which form the western sides of the **Santa Lucia Mountains,** drop abruptly into the ocean.

The 550-mile-long San Andreas fault follows the western side of the **Diablo Range,** turns slightly more eastward at the south end of the **San Joaquin Valley** along the transverse ranges (e.g., the **San Rafael** and **Tehachapi Mountains**), and curves gently toward the Gulf of California. Geologic evidence shows land to the west of the fault has moved north as much as 350 miles.

The **Sierra Nevada** are highest to the south. **Mt. Whitney** (14,496 ft.) is the highest point in conterminous 48 states. The Sierra Nevada end as though cut off by the Garlock Fault which, with the San Andreas Fault, define the high **Mojave Desert** wedge just north of **Los Angeles.**

The Channel Islands are remnants of the California Coast mountains. Much of the west coast is cliffs and mountains rising and wearing away (unlike the Atlantic coast which shows drowned valleys and floodplains, characteristics of a sinking coast). Geologists claim this results from a westward movement of the North American Continent of about 3 inches per year. The west coast is the leading edge and the east coast is the trailing edge of the continent.

Cotton and citrus fruits are grown in the **San Joaquin Valley,** the southern half of the Great Central Valley of California. The larger field pattern in the **Tulare Basin** reflects a more recent survey, whereas the surrounding farmland has been sectioned off into half mile squares.

The **California Aqueduct** runs along the western edge of the **San Joaquin Valley,** carrying water from the Sacramento River in the north for agriculture and for commercial use in the heavily populated southland. The **California Aqueduct** meets the **Los Angeles Aqueduct** at the western corner of the **Mojave Desert.** The **Los Angeles Aqueduct** brings water from the Owens River north of **Owens Lake.**

Pacific Ocean

The Canadians practice lumbering differently than Americans. This is shown in the absence of clear cut logging scars north of the international border, especially in the **Kootenai River Valley** where the graphic borderline has been removed. The mountain slopes on the American side of the border would be as dark as on the Canadian side if it were not for clear cut logging.

Seashells and fossil fish are found on the tops of the peaks in **Glacier National Park,** and ancient layers, more than a billion years old, lie over much younger strata which is 30 to 50 million years old. The younger rocks, formed of ancient sea bottom, were displaced more than 40 miles eastward, sliding over the older rock, while the whole mass was being elevated. Erosion by glaciers carved the mass into the beautiful mountains of today. Over 55 active glaciers remain, but they are small remnants of the original ones.

The largest lake in Idaho is **Lake Pend Oreille,** with an 111-mile shoreline. This lake is the home of the largest species of trout in the world, the Kamloop Rainbow Trout.

Lake Coeur d'Alene, in the Idaho Panhandle, is one of the most beautiful lakes in the world. On the northern shore of the lake is the city of **Coeur d'Alene,** which received a stampede of fortune seekers when silver was discovered there in 1884. The Sunshine Mine east of Coeur d'Alene is one of the largest silver mines in the United States. Idaho leads the nation in the production of silver.

North of the **Snake River** in **Washington** is the **Palouse** (grassland) country. The **Palouse** was originally used for ranchland until it was discovered that the rich organic soil was ideal for growing grain and peas. The alternating dark and light pattern of fallowed and planted wheat fields is visible on this photo-map.

The scablands, between the **Grand Coulee** (see photo-map pp. 6-7) and the **Palouse,** is a region of southwest trending dry channels formed by water from glaciers that reached as far south as the **Spokane River.** The channeled scablands appear on this photo-map as a webbing of dark, broad stripes.

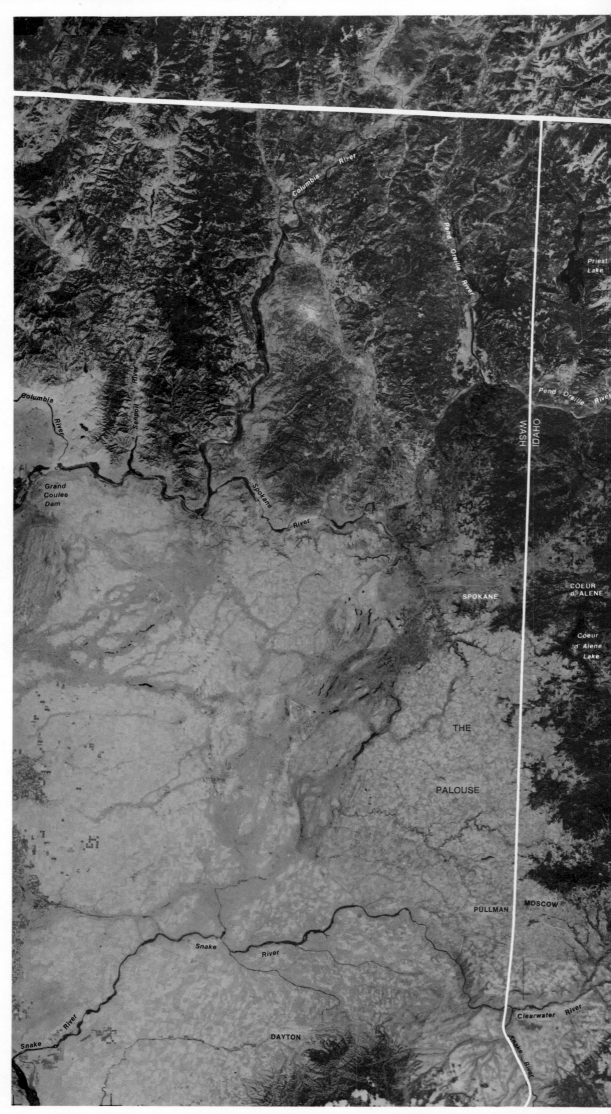

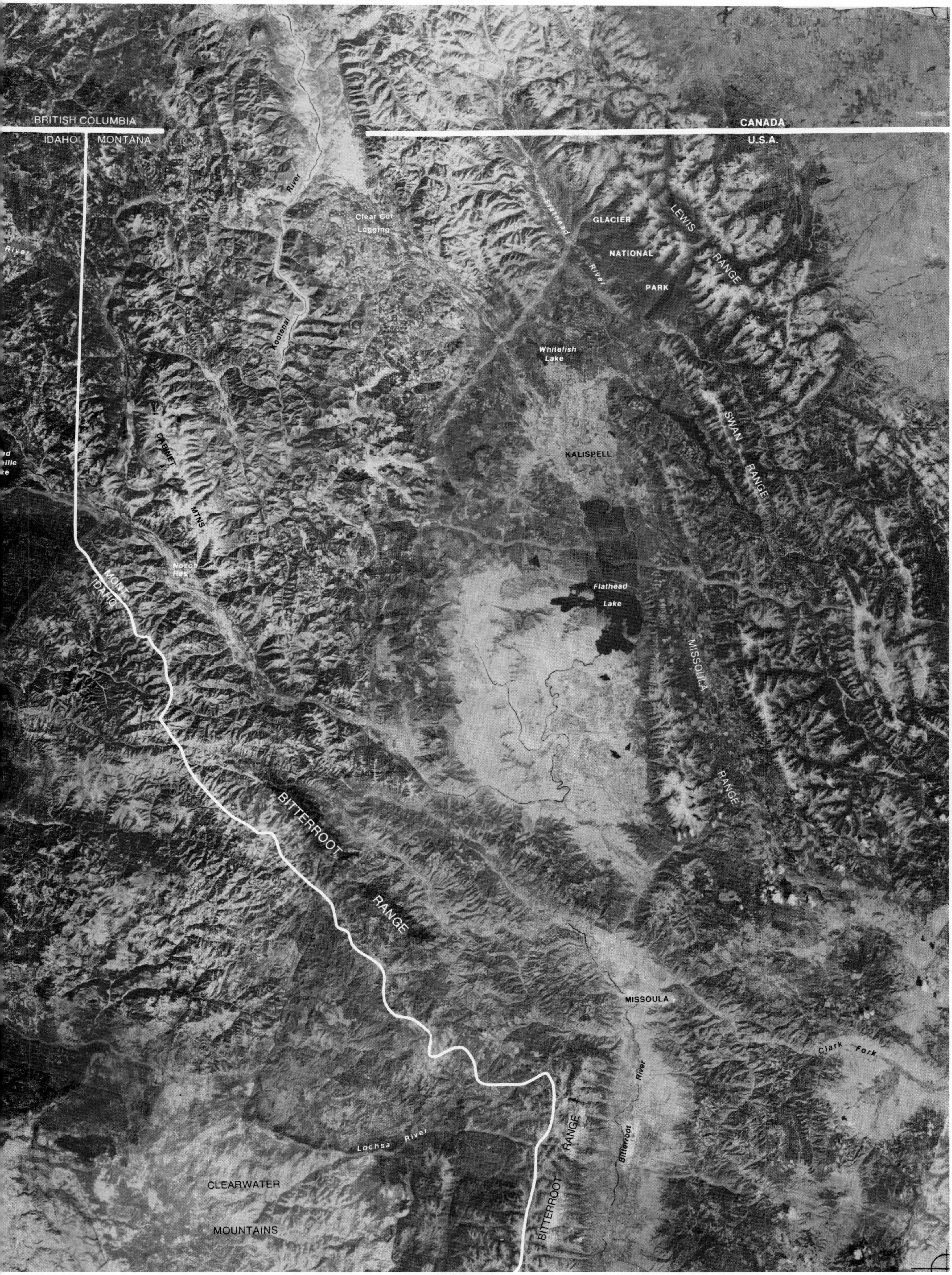

BRITISH COLUMBIA

IDAHO MONTANA

CANADA

U.S.A.

River

Clear Cut
Logging

Flathead

River

GLACIER

NATIONAL

PARK

LEWIS

RANGE

Whitefish
Lake

SWAN

RANGE

Kootenai

CABINET

MTNS

KALISPELL

Noxon
Res

Flathead
Lake

MISSOULA

MONT

IDAHO

BITTERROOT

RANGE

RANGE

MISSOULA

Clark Fork

BITTERROOT

RANGE

River

Bitterroot

Lochsa River

CLEARWATER

MOUNTAINS

Bitter Lake
Carkeek Park
Puget Sound
Pontiac Bay
Sand Point
JUANITA
Shilshole Bay
Green Lake
Woodland Park
KIRKLAND
Lake Washington
West Point
Lake Washington Canal
Fort Lawton
Univ of Washington
HOUGHTON
Union Bay
Cozy Cove
Evergreen Point Bridge
Lake Union
Volunteer Park
MEDINA
BELLEVUE
Seattle Center
SEATTLE
Elliott Bay
Leschi Park
Pioneer Square
Duwamish Head
Harbor Island
Lake Washington Bridge
Sunset Hwy
Alki Point
WEST SEATTLE
Jefferson Park Golf Course
Seward Park
Mercer Island
West Seattle Golf Course
Duwamish Waterway
Lincoln Park
Lake Boren
BOEING FIELD
Brace Point
May Creek
BRYN MAWR
Rainier Golf Course
Puget Sound
Renton Mun. Airport
RENTON
RIVERTON HEIGHTS
Cedar River
Point Beals
Vashon Island
Lake Burien
Longacres Race Track
Three Tree Point
SEA-TAC INT'L AIRPORT
NORMANDY PARK
Green River

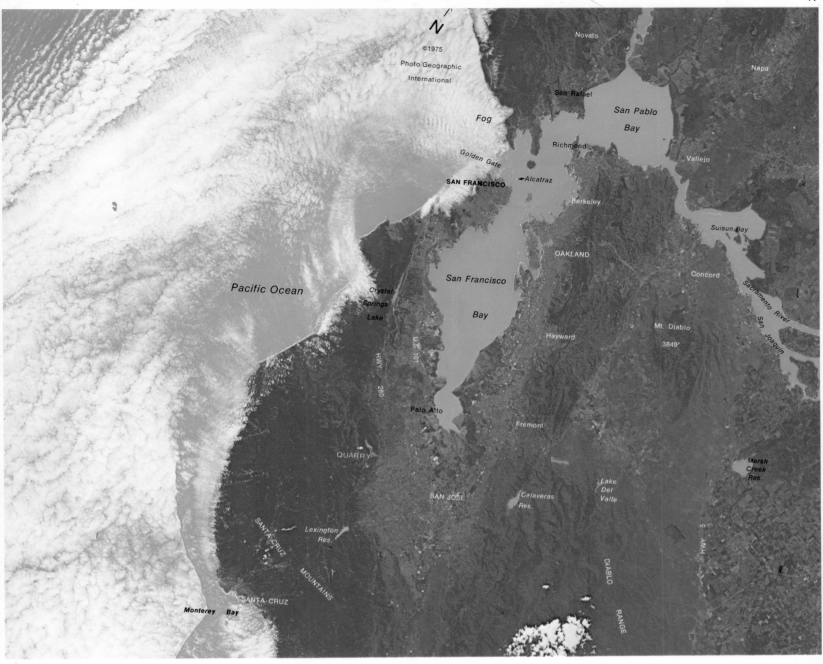

©1975
Photo Geographic
International

Seattle

In 1851, the first settlement in the **Seattle** area was established at **Alki Point.** Alki was the Indian term for by and by. Originally called New York Alki because of its superficial geographic similarities to New York (see New York photo-map page 110) the more permanent settlement of **Seattle** was established near **Pioneer Square** in 1852 and the city began its first boom in 1898 after gold was discovered in the Alaskan Klondike.

Though more than 100 miles from the open ocean, Seattle's protected location on **Puget Sound** has helped to make it an important seaport. Locks extended ocean shipping into **Lake Union** and **Lake Washington** after 1916 and these freshwater lakes served to remove saltwater barnacles from ships' hulls without costly and time-consuming dry-docking.

Though **Seattle** is located at the same latitude as Montreal, Canada, winds from the Pacific and the Japanese Current moderate its climate to an average of fifty-degree temperatures. The Olympic Mountains to the west capture up to 100 inches of precipitation each year, sparing **Seattle** no more than about 35 inches of drizzly rainfall. The cool, overcast weather and the hills of Seattle remind one of San Francisco.

The **Seattle Center,** southwest of **Lake Union,** was the site of the 1962 Seattle World's Fair. The Space Needle, symbol of the fair, remains.

Two floating bridges span **Lake Washington. Evergreen Point Bridge,** the northernmost, is the world's longest floating bridge with 35 pontoon units stretching for 6,500 feet. The completion of these bridges created a residential and commercial sprawl east from Seattle. The accessibility of **Mercer Island,** via the **Lake Washington Bridge,** prompted development of an exclusive residential area.

Between **Interstate 5** and the **Duwamish Waterway** is **Boeing Field.**

San Francisco

The **Golden Gate** and **San Francisco Bay** provide the only breach in the Coastal Ranges of California from the Oregon border to Santa Barbara. The sheltered anchorage has encouraged both **San Francisco** and **Oakland** to become important world ports. **San Jose,** at the southern tip of the bay, has grown from a population of 90,000 in 1950 to a sprawling city of a half million in the early 1970's.

The chilly waters of the **Golden Gate** race in and out with the tides at speeds up to 6 knots. This made escape from the prison on **Alcatraz Island** almost impossible.

Movement along the **San Andreas** fault caused the 1906 San Francisco earthquake. The fault follows a line through the center of the peninsula, under **Crystal Springs Lake,** and into the ocean at the southwest corner of **San Francisco.**

The salt evaporators of southern **San Francisco Bay** are often red because of an algae that thrives in salty water.

The **Sacramento** and **San Joaquin Rivers** empty into the Delta Region, east of **San Pablo Bay.** Land in this region has been reclaimed and made usable by dikes and canals.

The **San Jose Airport** ranks seventh nationally in total number of take-offs and landings. **San Francisco International** ranks tenth.

A large mothball fleet of World War II Liberty ships is moored in the Sacramento River just northeast of San Pablo Bay. They appear as rows of white dots on this photo-map.

The large, light brown mark in the **Santa Cruz Mountains,** southeast of **Palo Alto,** is a **quarry** for a cement company. Smoke from that cement company can be seen just south of the quarry.

Pendleton, Oregon is the center of a large sheep ranching area which extends into the **Blue Mountains.** The city has long been famous for its fine woolen textiles and shirts, and for its annual fair and rodeo, called the Pendleton Roundup.

The **Salmon River** in central Idaho is known as the River of No Return, because of its rapids and treacherous falls. Lewis and Clark explored the region in 1805. They attempted to navigate the river but were forced to retreat after 50 miles.

The valleys south of the **Columbia** and **Snake Rivers** and the beautiful **Wallowa Mountains** are the home of the peaceful Nez Perce Indians. In 1877 the harassment of these people forced Chief Joseph to lead them on a 1,700 mile retreat, hoping for asylum in Canada. Although he successfully outwitted, outfought and outmaneuvered his more numerous enemies, he was finally halted about 50 miles from Canada. This photo-map and photo-maps on pp. 32-33 and pp. 34-35 show the seemingly impassible terrain that the Nez Perce people crossed during their 17 month journey.

Hells Canyon on the **Snake River** is the deepest gorge in the United States, reaching depths up to 7,900 feet. **Mt. Borah,** in the **Los River Range,** is the highest mountain in Idaho at 12,600 ft. The ski resort of Sun Valley, in the **Smokey Mountains,** is located about 50 miles (2 inches on the photo-map) north of **Magic Reservoir.**

Boise is the financial and trading center of Idaho and eastern Oregon. Extensive agriculture is visable west of the city along the **Snake** and **Boise Rivers.** Grains, vegetables, fruits, and dairy products are grown here.

Craters of the Moon National Monument, seen in the southeast portion of the photo-map, is an area of prehistoric volcanic activity. It was named in pre-astronaut days when the beds of lava, ash and pumice were thought to resemble the terrain on the moon. Astronauts preparing for moon landings trained here. Although exploration of the moon revealed that the monument does not much resemble the lunar landscape, the name was retained.

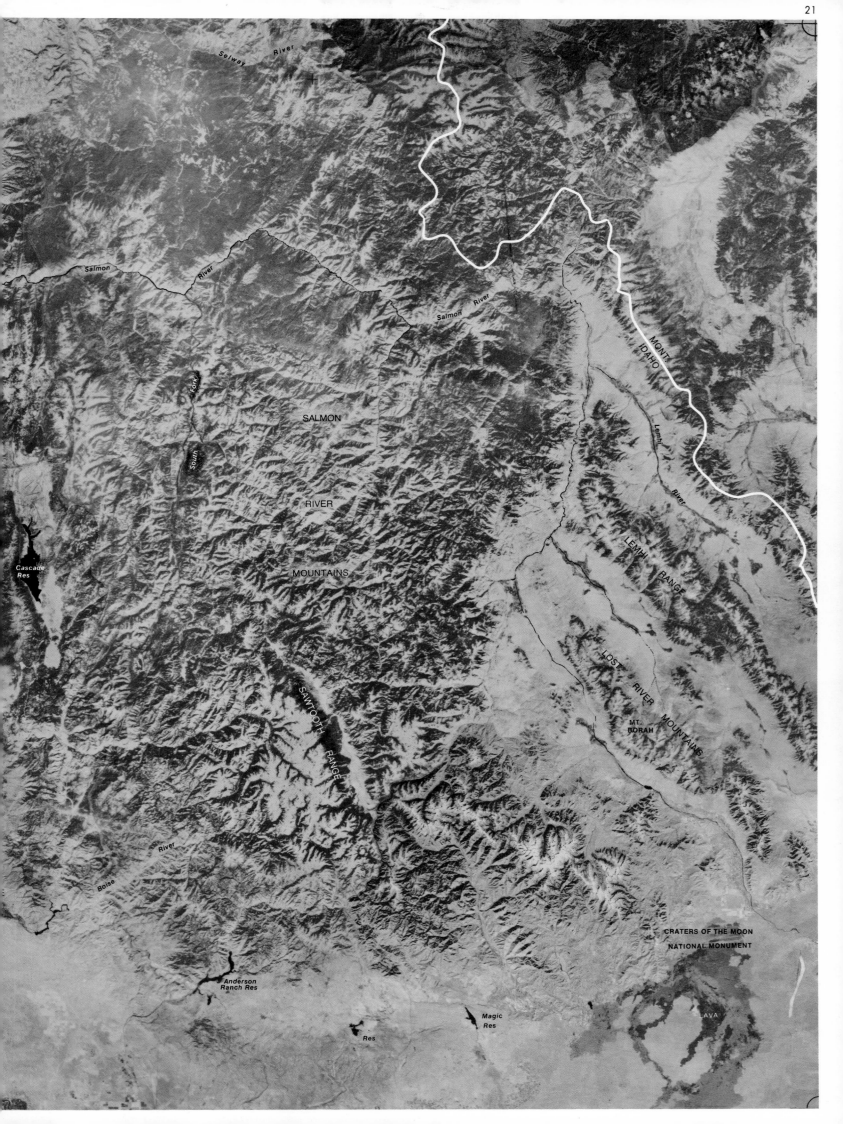

Selway River

Salmon River

Salmon River

Salmon

South Fork

SALMON

RIVER

MOUNTAINS

Cascade Res

MONT
IDAHO

Lemhi

River

LEMHI RANGE

LOST RIVER MOUNTAINS

MT. BORAH

SAWTOOTH RANGE

Boise River

Anderson Ranch Res

Magic Res

Res

CRATERS OF THE MOON

NATIONAL MONUMENT

LAVA

SANTA MONICA MOUNTAINS

SANTA

Stone
Canyon
Res.

Hollywood
Res.

Hollywood

Franklin
Canyon
Res.

WEST
HOLLYWOOD

Sunset Blvd.

Hollywood Fwy.

BEVERLY HILLS

PACIFIC
PALISADES

San Diego Fwy.

U.C.L.A.

L.A. Golf
Course

Wilshire
Golf
Course

Brentwood
Golf Course

20th
Century Fox

Wilshire Blvd.

TOPANGA
BEACH

Santa Monica Fwy.

SANTA
MONICA

Santa Monica
Airport

CULVER
CITY

U.S.

BALDWIN HILLS

Exposition
Park

Santa

Ballona Creek

Hughes
Airport

INGLEWOOD

Marina
del Rey

Loyola
Univ.

The Forum

Monica

PLAYA
DEL REY

Hollywood Park
Race Track

Pacific
Ocean

LOS ANGELES
INT'L AIRPORT

San Diego Fwy.

Bay

EL SEGUNDO

Hawthorne
Mun. Airport

HAWTHORNE

MANHATTAN
BEACH

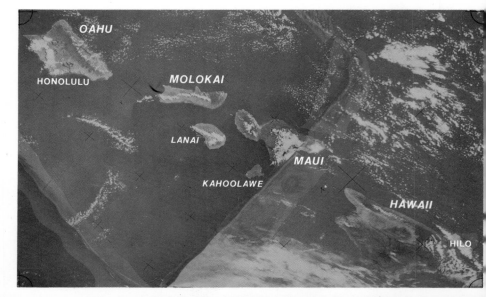

OAHU

HONOLULU

MOLOKAI

LANAI

MAUI

KAHOOLAWE

HAWAII

HILO

Los Angeles

Sprawling **Los Angeles,** with a metropolitan area approaching 2,000 square miles and made up of some 90 cities, is the product of urbanization in the auto age. Flexibility of travel by private auto encouraged the city to rapidly fill the low-lying areas and spread into the adjacent foothills. Los Angeles' metropolitan area population density is about 5,000 people per square mile compared to 16,500 in San Francisco and 76,000 in Manhattan.

To the north of **Los Angeles** can be seen the **Santa Monica Mountains,** uncommonly oriented in an east-west direction.

Water, particularly in the dry summer season, is a major problem for the Los Angeles area. Great amounts of water must be imported via aqueducts and canals to storage reservoirs like **Stone Canyon, Hollywood,** and **Franklin Canyon.**

Because **Los Angeles** sits in a natural basin ringed by mountains, except on its Pacific side, there is a lack of air circulation peculiar to this area. Thus, when an inversion layer caps the basin, causing stagnation of the air and trapping exhausts and other pollutants, the infamous smog, which covers **Los Angeles** about 200 days a year, is quickly formed.

Santa Monica Bay is rimmed by miles of sandy beaches forming the recreation and residential area called the Strand.

In the southern portion of this photo-map, extending east from the coast, is the large oil refinery at **El Segundo** with its numerous circular storage tanks. This is Southern California's largest refinery.

Hawaii

An almost continual presence of clouds over the Hawaiian Islands hinders the collection of photography for a cloud-free photo-map. These two photos from handheld Skylab cameras nevertheless capture the beautiful colors of the Islands.

The Hawaiian Islands are volcanic in origin. Current geologic theory contends that the floor of the Pacific Ocean has been moving to the northwest over a hot spot at the rate of about 2 inches per year. Islands are created by vulcanism as the ocean floor passes over this hot spot. This explains the current volcanic activity near the southwest shore of the big island, **Hawaii.** Streaks of ancient lava flows crossing the islands are visible on the photo-map.

The farm land seen in the northeastern portion of this photo-map produces seed beans and Irish potatoes. The organic soil of this region, irrigated by the water from the **Snake River,** enables Idaho to lead the nation in potato production.

The **Humboldt River,** crossing the center of this photo-map, was part of the California Trail used by the 49'ers seeking California's gold. The trail followed the river west for 350 miles until the river was reduced to a trickle and evaporated in the desert near **Carson Sink.** This disappointed many thirsty 49'ers who never knew a river could disappear without leading them to the sea.

The **Carson Sink** and other alkali flats between the mountain ranges are dry salt lakes most of the year, but receive some moisture during the winter months. Also known as Playas, the Spanish word for beach, these flats are sometimes red because of a salt-water algae and because of iron-bearing deposits eroded from the nearby mountains.

Along the eastern border of this photo-map is the **Great Salt Lake Desert** of northwestern Utah. the Great Salt Lake Desert (see photo-map pp. 32-33) is a remnant of ancient Lake Bonneville, which at its high-water stages rose 100 feet above the present Great Salt Lake, entirely submersing the area which is now desert.

The **Bonneville Salt Flats** Race Track, near the Utah-Nevada border, is the site of automobile speed and endurance trails.

The mountain ridges and valleys in the southern half of this photo-map are the northern part of the Basin and Range Region. The basins are downdropped blocks between the upraised blocks of the ranges. Geologists call such alternating fault blocks Horst and Graben.

The numerous uninhabited mountain ranges of Nevada are homes for wild mustangs. These mustangs were once hunted for pet food, but a 1971 law protecting wild horses may insure their survival.

The extensive grasslands of northern Nevada are ideal for livestock. Cattle and sheep raising are significant factors in the economy of towns like **Elko** and **Winnemucca.**

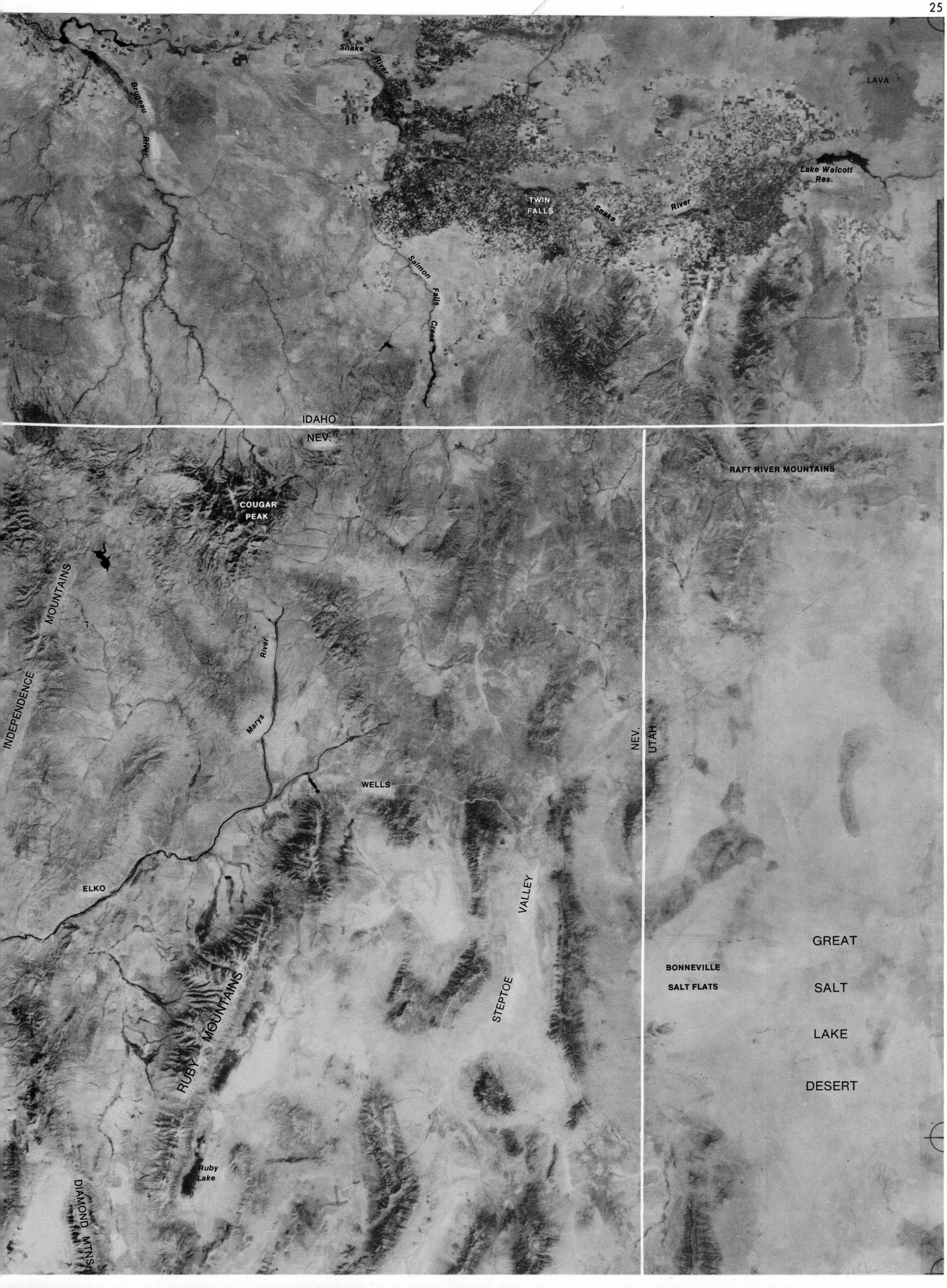

Snake River

LAVA

TWIN
FALLS

Snake

River

Lake Walcott
Res.

Bruneau

River

Salmon

Falls

Creek

IDAHO

NEV.

COUGAR
PEAK

RAFT RIVER MOUNTAINS

INDEPENDENCE

MOUNTAINS

River

Marys

WELLS

NEV.

UTAH

ELKO

VALLEY

GREAT

STEPTOE

BONNEVILLE

SALT FLATS

SALT

RUBY MOUNTAINS

LAKE

DESERT

Ruby
Lake

DIAMOND MTNS.

Winds from the west lose most of their moisture when crossing the **Sierra Nevada,** creating desert-like conditions for most of Nevada. The annual rainfall for the state is less than 10 inches. Vegetation consists mainly of salt brush and greasewood in the lowlands and scrub oak and ponderosa in the mountains.

The **Stillwater Range, Clan Alpine Mountains, Shoshone Mountains,** etc., form the western edge of the Basin and Range Region, a series of mountain ridges and valleys running northeast. Some geologists believe that this ridge and valley system represents wrinkles in the upper crust of the earth caused by movement of the North American continent. The crust is relatively thin in this area.

This entire photo-map is a good example of the Basin and Range geologic province which includes Nevada and western Utah. The extent of the Basin and Range Region can be seen on the index photo-map on pages 4 and 5.

Deposits of gold and silver worth billions of dollars have been found scattered throughout the state of Nevada. The hills and flat lowlands in the southern half of this photo-map have been mined extensively.

Today, Nevada's most valuable metal is copper. The light colored, stripped area on the photo-map slightly northwest of **Ely,** Nevada, is the Liberty Pit. This mine, one of the largest open pit copper mines in the world, has been worked since 1900 and is over 800 feet deep.

On the upper ridges of the **White Mountains** are found the bristlecone pine trees, the oldest living things on Earth. Some of these trees are nealy 5,000 years old. In Kings Canyon (see photo-map pp. 12-13), just 50 miles to the southwest, are the largest living things on Earth, the giant sequoia trees.

Irrigation can be seen in the valley west of the **Diamond Mountains** and in the valley south of the **Needle Mountains.** There is considerable geothermal activity in this part of the United States. The popular baths of **Hot Creek,** in the **Hot Creek Range,** are a result of this.

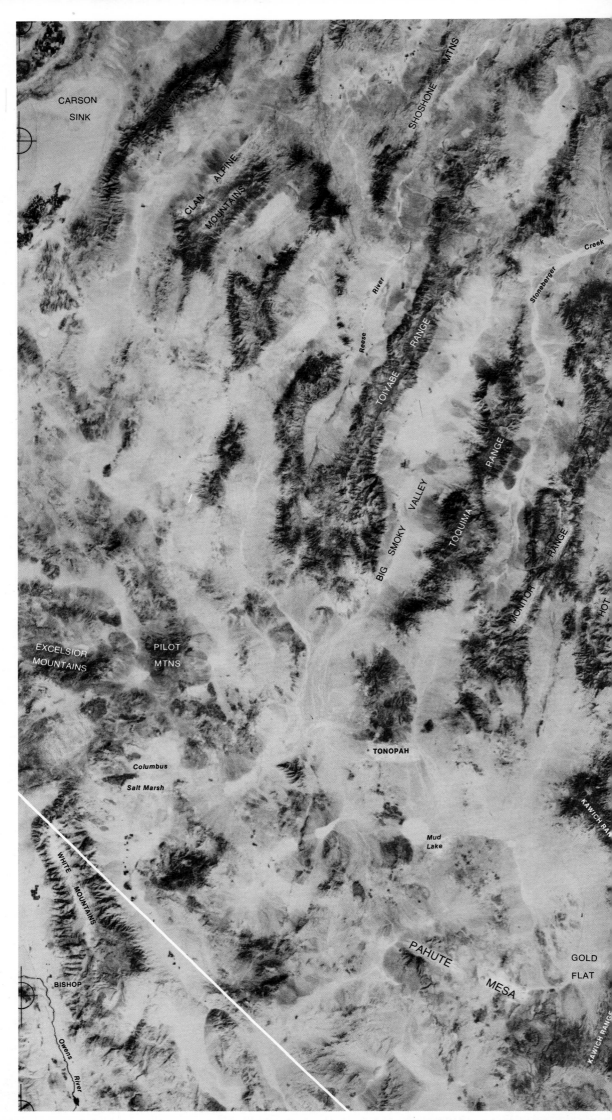

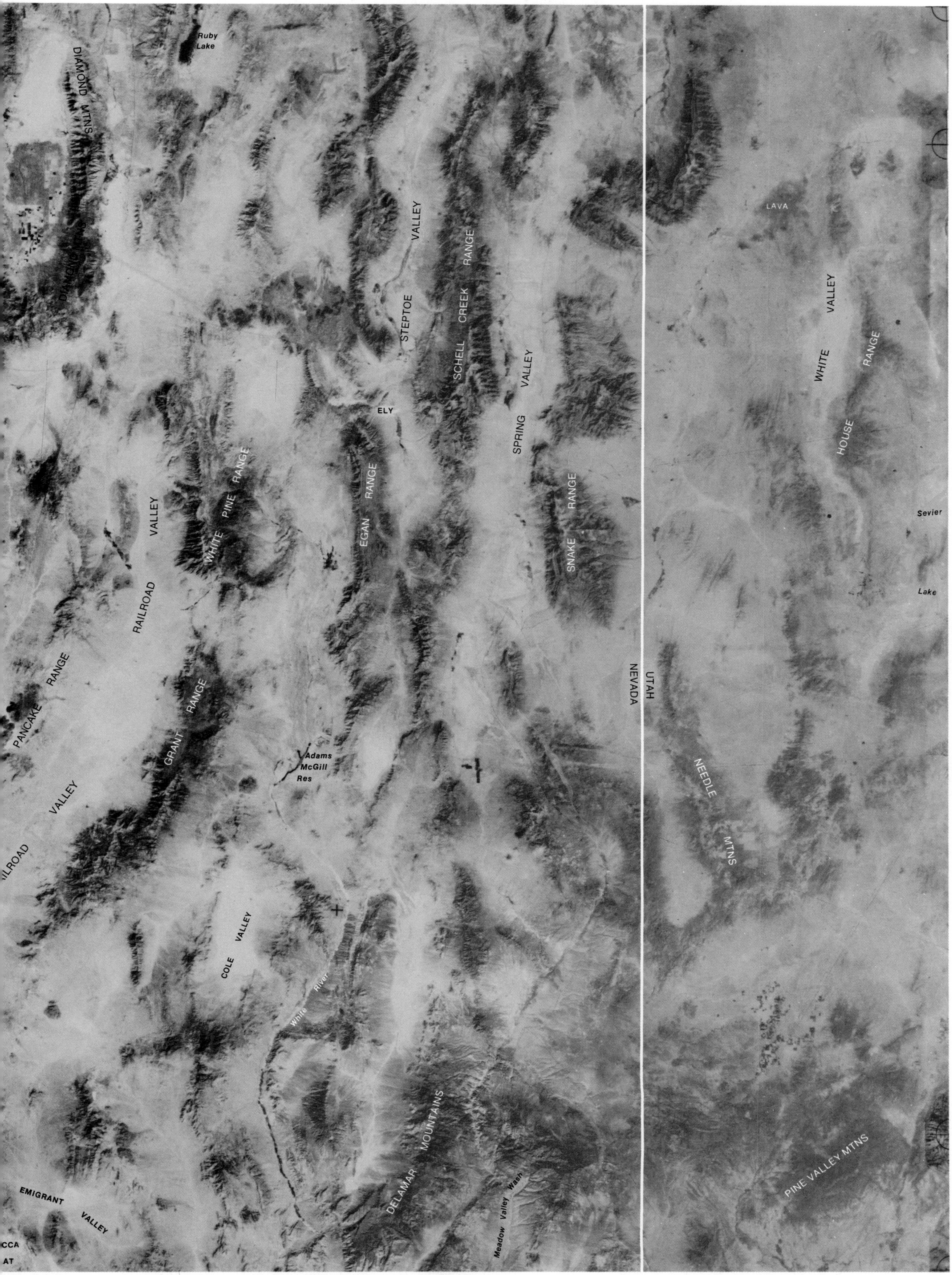

Ruby
Lake

DIAMOND MTNS

DIAMOND

STEPTOE VALLEY

SCHELL CREEK RANGE

LAVA

WHITE VALLEY

HOUSE RANGE

ELY

WHITE PINE RANGE

EGAN RANGE

SPRING VALLEY

SNAKE RANGE

Sevier

Lake

VALLEY

RAILROAD

PANCAKE RANGE

GRANT RANGE

NEVADA

UTAH

Adams
McGill
Res

VALLEY

NEEDLE

MTNS

RAILROAD

COLE VALLEY

White River

DELAMAR MOUNTAINS

Meadow Valley Wash

EMIGRANT

VALLEY

PINE VALLEY MTNS

CCA

AT

Mt. Witney is the highest peak in the U.S. outside of Alaska. Just 60 miles to the east is **Death Valley,** the lowest point in the U.S., with an elevation of 282 feet below sea level. Drainage from nearly 9,000 square miles runs into the valley to evaporate.

In addition to gold and silver, minerals in this region include salines such as borax.

The **Mojave Desert** is shaped like a wedge pointing west. It is bounded on the north by the Garlock Fault and on the south by the San Andreas Fault.

The **Mojave,** like most American deserts, is not regarded as a real desert by people who have studied the deserts of other parts of the world. Unlike the Sahara, the Gobi, or the Takla Makan Desert of China, our deserts have abundant and varied vegetation and receive small but dependably regular precipitation. After a rainy season the **Mojave** can become a vast flower garden.

Through the area of this photo-map and of photo-maps to the east, there are hundreds of lost mines and lost treasures. Many are legendary, but some, no doubt, are actual. From the earliest days of the European exploration, Indians were enslaved and employed in mining and smelting ores for white masters. The bullion thus recovered was frequently stored away in caves, etc. A single massacre by natives uninterested in bullion could erase all knowledge of such treasure.

Lake Mead was formed in the Colorado River by the construction of Hoover (Boulder) Dam in 1936. The dam caused the flooding of many canyons and gorges downstream from the Grand Canyon.

The flats north of **Mercury,** Nevada is where the Atomic Energy Commission conducts tests of atomic weapons. Land or air traffic over the entire area around **Yucca Flat** is restricted. (Space traffic is not.)

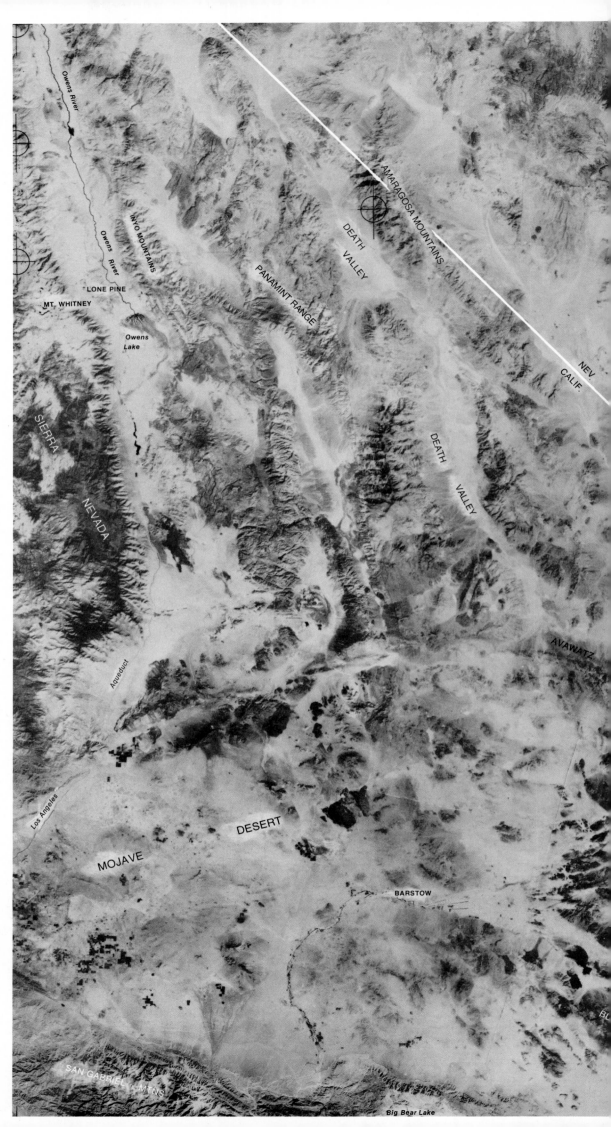

EMIGRANT VALLEY

CCA

AT

MERCURY

SPRING MOUNTAINS

LAS VEGAS

PROVIDENCE MOUNTAINS

PLAYGROUND

LAVA

TURTLE MTNS

DELAMAR MTNS

SHEEP RANGE

MORMON MTNS

Lake Mead

Colorado River

Lake Mohave

CALIF ARIZ

Lake Havasu

NEV. UTAH

PINE VALLEY MTNS

Virgin River

VIRGIN MTNS

LAVA

Colorado River

GRAND WASH CLIFFS

HUALAPAI MOUNTAINS

SAN GABRIEL MTNS

SANTA MONICA MTNS

Big Bear Lake

SAN BERNARDINO

SAN BERNARDINO MTNS

RIVERSIDE

LOS ANGELES

PALM SPRINGS

JO

LONG
BEACH

SAN JACINTO MTNS

SANTA ANA MTNS

Lake
Elsinor

Santa Catalina
Island

Dana Pt

SAN CLEMENTE

LAGUNA MTNS

Gulf of

San Clemente
Island

Santa Catalina

SAN DIEGO

CALIF.

BAJA CALIFORNIA

TIJUANA

Islas

Pacific Ocean

Los

Coronados

SIERRA DE

Land routes from the north and the east into southern California must cross or skirt the transverse mountain ranges shown in the northeastern portion of this photo-map (also see photo map pp. 14-15). Natural mountain passes, such as the Cajon Pass between the **San Gabriel** and **San Bernadino Ranges,** have helped create pass towns like **San Bernadino,** which

gain economic support because they are located at the base of a highland crossing for rail and highway transportation.

The **Imperial Valley** was a desert 100 years ago, but like most American deserts, the soil was good. By 1900, the **Colorado River** was successfully dammed and the water was distributed over a wide area. Thus the **Imperial Valley** became a center

for various truck garden crops such as lettuce and tomatoes. The consequent pollution of such irrigation run-off is sent back into the **Colorado River** and Mexican farmers complain that they get our problems instead of pure water. A distinction in agricultural quality can be seen on this photo-map where the international boundary crosses the **Imperial Valley.**

1905, the Colorado irriga-
al system broke down and
led the area to the north-
, which was much lower
the river itself. This water,
some years, grew salty
the **Salton Sea** is now a
anent lake, 234 feet below
evel.

e **Salton Sea** lies in the high
of a large trough filled by
Gulf of California to the

south (see the Index Map on pp.
4-5). The San Andreas Fault runs
through the mountains east of
the **Salton Sea.**

The **All American Canal,** 80
miles long and 200 feet wide,
now transports **Colorado River**
water to irrigate the **Imperial
Valley.**

San Diego, the oldest city in
California, was founded as the
first of the California missions in

1769. **San Diego Bay** provides an
excellent natural harbor for the
large naval base installed there.
The Bay is also the center of a
vast tuna fishing fleet. Specially
built tuna clippers range far into
the South Pacific and regularly
make their catches in the waters
off Ecuador, Peru, and Chile.

This photo-map shows the western edge of the Great Plains, where layers of sedimentary rock tilt up toward the Rocky Mountains. In the western high plains, mountains are evidence of thermal activity below the surface crust of the Earth. The **Bear Paw Mountains** are of volcanic origin. The **Little Rockies,** the **Big Snowies,** the **Little Belt Mountains,** and other mountains shown here are unwarped domes and arches of sedimentary rock (miniature versions of the Black Hills in South Dakota).

The small mountain ranges on this photo-map are circular or are elongated in an east-west direction. The Rocky Mountains, immediately to the west (also see photo-map pp. 16-17), have north-south trending features. The accordian-like folds in the mountains west of the **Sun** and **Teton Rivers** are possibly the result of subterranean thermal activity forcing this portion of the Great Plains in a westerly direction.

The very wide part of the **Missouri River** (on the right) is actually the upper reaches of the **Fort Peck Reservior.** This reservoir is held by the 242-foot-high Fort Peck Dam, one of the highest earth-fill dams ever built (see photo-map pp. 44-45).

The route of Lewis and Clark's 1806 explorations follows the **Missouri River** from right to left across this photo-map.

Fort Benton, at the junction of the **Missouri** and **Teton Rivers,** was built at the beginning of navigation on the **Missouri.** Upstream from here is the **Great Falls** white water area.

In the gulches along the west side of the **Big Belt Mountains,** gold was discovered in 1864. The strike yielded over $15,000,000 and set off the Montana mining boom, which attracted many veterans of the Civil War.

The graphic borderline has been removed from the Canadian Border east of the **Sweet Grass Hills,** showing a distinction between U.S. and Canadian agriculture. Apparently, wheat farming is not economical just north of the border.

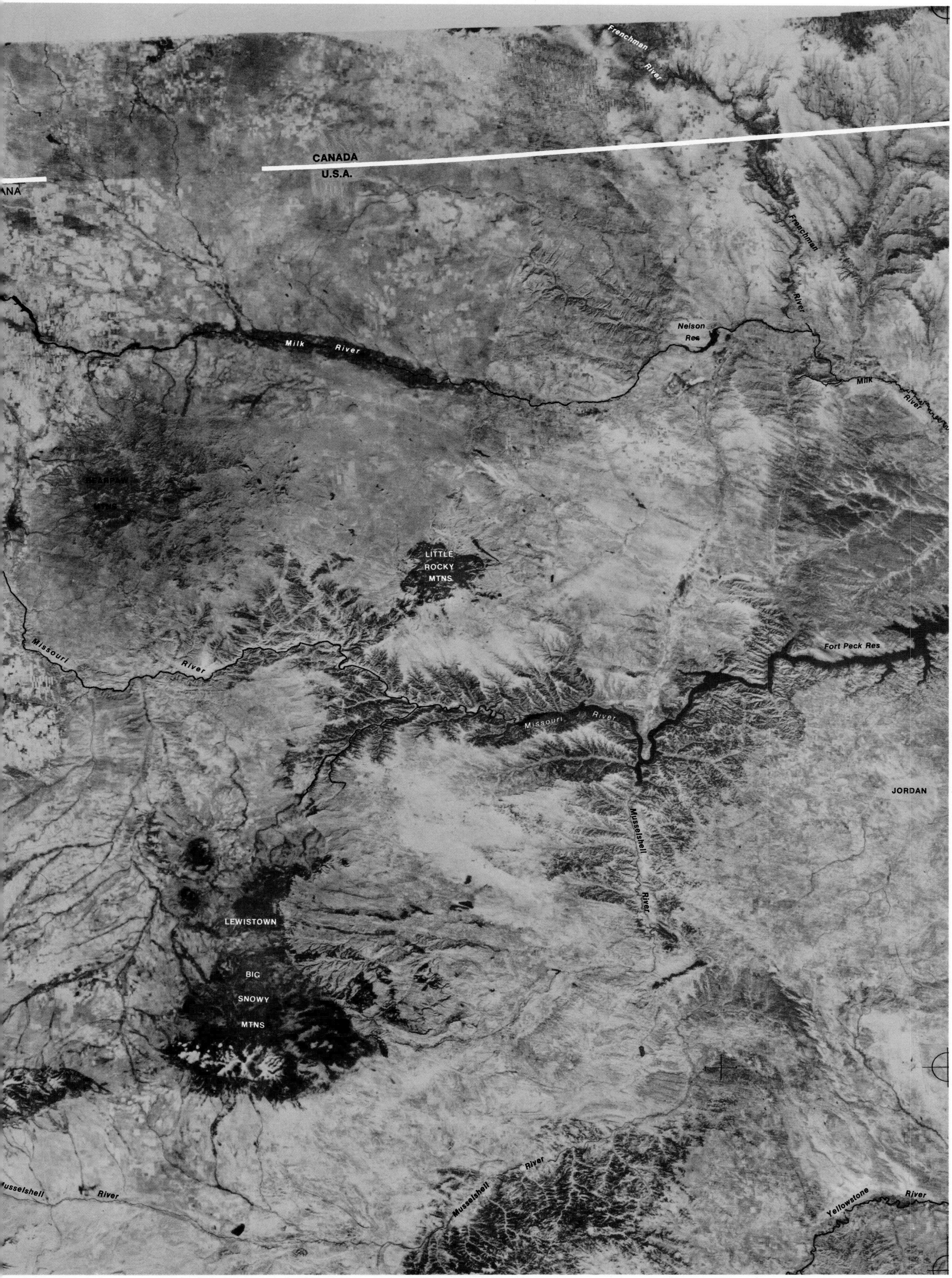

33

CANADA

U.S.A.

ANA

Frenchman River

Frenchman River

Milk River

Nelson Res

Milk River

BEARPAW MTNS

LITTLE ROCKY MTNS

Missouri River

Fort Peck Res

Missouri River

JORDAN

Musselshell River

LEWISTOWN

BIG SNOWY MTNS

Musselshell River

Musselshell River

Yellowstone River

The **Continental Divide** roughly follows the western edges of this photo-map and of the photo-map on pp. 32-33. The Divide angles south-eastward defining the Idaho-Montana border, passes through Wyoming between **Shoshone Lake** and **Yellowstone Lake** and then heads south along the eastern Rocky Mountains.

The area east of the Continental Divide on this photo-map and neighboring photo-maps to the north and east is the Missouri River Basin, the largest watershed in the United States. The Red Rock River, in the southeastern portion of this photo-map, is the headstream of the Missouri River.

Yellowstone, the first National Park, includes spectacular gorges, falls and many geysers. Along with Iceland and the Rotorua area of New Zealand, this is one of the most extensive areas of geothermal activity in the world. It was first explored in 1807 by John Colter of the Lewis and Clark expedition. Ground water, heated by volcanism, produces fumaroles and steam for geysers. The region is named for the sulfur-bearing yellow rock visible in this photo-map as bright specks around **Yellowstone Lake.**

Grasshopper Glacier, on the southwest slopes of the **Beartooth Mountains,** contains many layers of frozen grasshoppers. These insects, of the same type which destroyed Mormon crops, were probably trapped on their migrations by early freezes and snows.

Southeast of **Hardin,** Montana, up the **Little Big Horn River** (about one inch on this photomap), is the Custer Battlefield National Monument. In June 1876, George Armstrong Custer led 208 men into an ambush by about 600 warriors led by Sitting Bull. The arrogant Army officer did not consider the ease with which large forces could be concealed in the eroded terrain (visible on the photo-map) of this region.

The **Madison River** flows from the northwest arm of **Hebgen Lake.** In 1958 a severe earthquake caused a large landslide which buried three dozen or more campers and dammed the river. The resulting lake is called **Earthquake Lake.**

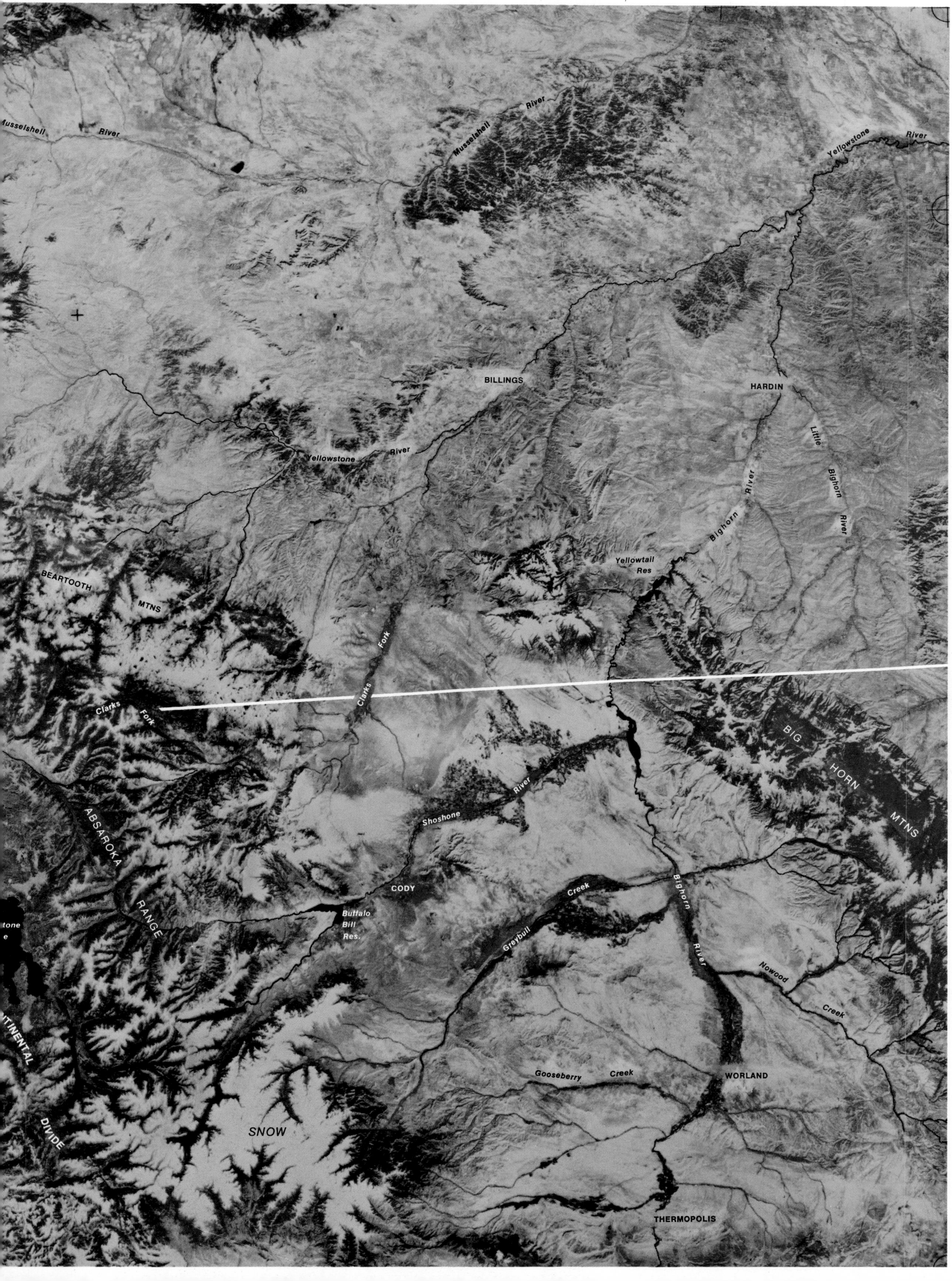

Musselshell River

Musselshell River

Yellowstone River

BILLINGS

HARDIN

Little

Bighorn

River

Yellowstone River

Bighorn

River

BEARTOOTH

MTNS

Yellowtail Res

Clarks Fork

BIG

HORN

MTNS

Clarks Fork

ABSAROKA

RANGE

Shoshone River

stone e

CODY

Greybull Creek

Bighorn

River

Buffalo Bill Res.

Nowood

Creek

CONTINENTAL

DIVIDE

Gooseberry Creek

WORLAND

SNOW

THERMOPOLIS

Wyoming's highest point, **Gannett Peak,** rises from the 100-mile-long **Wind River Range.** The largest glaciers in the conterminous U.S. lie among the peaks of the **Wind River Range.** The western slopes include the 383,300-acre **Bridger Wilderness Area,** parts of which are used for grazing large flocks of sheep in the summer.

The **Continental Divide** follows the crest of Wyoming's **Wind River Range** and then becomes 2 divides, circling the **Great Divide Basin.** This basin is one area where the east-west division of water flow from the Divide is disrupted. Creeks drain into the basin and evaporate to form an alkaline desert with patches of sage and greasewood as the only vegetation.

The **Sweetwater River** flows east along the northern rim of the **Great Divide Basin,** and joins the **North Platte River** southwest of **Casper,** Wyoming (see photo-map pp. 48-49). The headwaters of the **Sweetwater River** begin at the southern tip of the **Wind River Range** near a natural break in the mountains called South Pass. This relatively easy route through the Rockies was used by thousands of pioneers following the Oregon Trail.

Great Salt Lake is a remnant of Lake Bonneville, a giant glacial lake which covered over 50,000 square miles. Lake Bonneville was a freshwater lake, but when it began to evaporate 25,000 years ago it became more salty. Today the lake is 5 to 6 times more salty than the oceans.

A railroad bridge, which is essentially a rock and earthen dam, crosses the **Great Salt Lake,** preventing the saltier water to the north from mixing with the water to the south. The algae that thrives in the saltier northern water is red. A blue-green algae occupies the water to the south of the bridge. The result is the two distinct shades of lake water seen in this photo-map.

The **Uinta Mountains** extend eastward in Utah below the Wyoming border. This mountain range, with elevations up to 13,500 feet, is unique among ranges in the Rocky Mountain system because it runs east to west. **King's Peak,** Utah's highest mountain, sits at the western end of the **Uintas.**

TRE RANGE

Boysen
Res

Wind

Badwater   Creek

River

GANNETT
PEAK

WIND RIVER RANGE

FORT WASHAKIE   RIVERTON

Fremont
Lake

CONTINENTAL

RATTLESNAKE
RANGE

PINEDALE

BRIDGER

NAT'L

DIVIDE

FOREST

Sweetwater   River

ER
L
ST

Big Sandy
Res.

GREAT   DIVIDE   BASIN

Fontonelle
Res.

Green

EMMERER

Hams

River

Bitter

Fork

ROCK SPRINGS   Creek

Flaming
Gorge
Res

WYOMING

Little   Snake   River

UTAH   COLORADO

Green

UINTA   MTNS

Henrys   Fork

River

KINGS
PEAK

DINOSAUR
NAT'L MON   Yampa   River

This photo-map, together with photo-maps on pp. 40-41 to the south and pp. 50-51 to the east, show some of the most spectacular scenery of the Colorado Plateau. The Colorado Plateau has risen more than a mile during the past 10 million years. A photo-map provides a unique perspective of the nature and extent of the erosion that has taken place while this region was rising.

Erosion by rivers have produced numerous arches or natural bridges, especially along the left side of this photo-map. North of **Moab,** Utah is **Arches National Monument** with Owachomo Bridge, one of the largest stone arches in the world. About 75 miles down the **Colorado River** and slightly to the east is **Natural Bridges National Monument** with many other stone arches.

Cedar Breaks National Monument, a large depression filled with eroded ridges visible here as bright streaks, is one of the most colorful sights in Utah.

A little east of **Cedar Breaks** lies **Bryce Canyon** National Park, a spectacular valley full of fantastic erosional sculptures of astonishing colors and ever-different scenes.

The farmland around **Provo,** Utah and to the north (see photo-map pp. 36-37) represents a somewhat miraculous feat of irrigation by the Mormon people. Water dropped by eastward moving clouds crossing the **Wasatch Mountains** is carefully distributed over this former desert land.

The two irrigated valleys near the center of this photo-map are both Federal Reclamation projects. The upper one, along the north side of the **Colorado River** is Grand Valley Reclamation Project, and the one extending south and east along the **Gunnison River** is Uncompahgre Reclamation Project.

Lake Powell extends for 160 miles in southern **Utah** (also see photo-map pp. 40-41). The lake was created by damming the **Colorado River** in Arizona and flooding **Glen Canyon.** The **Green River,** the Colorado's largest tributary by volume, begins in Wyoming's **Wind River Range** (see photo-map pp. 36-37) and flows south to its junction with the **Colorado River** above **Lake Powell.**

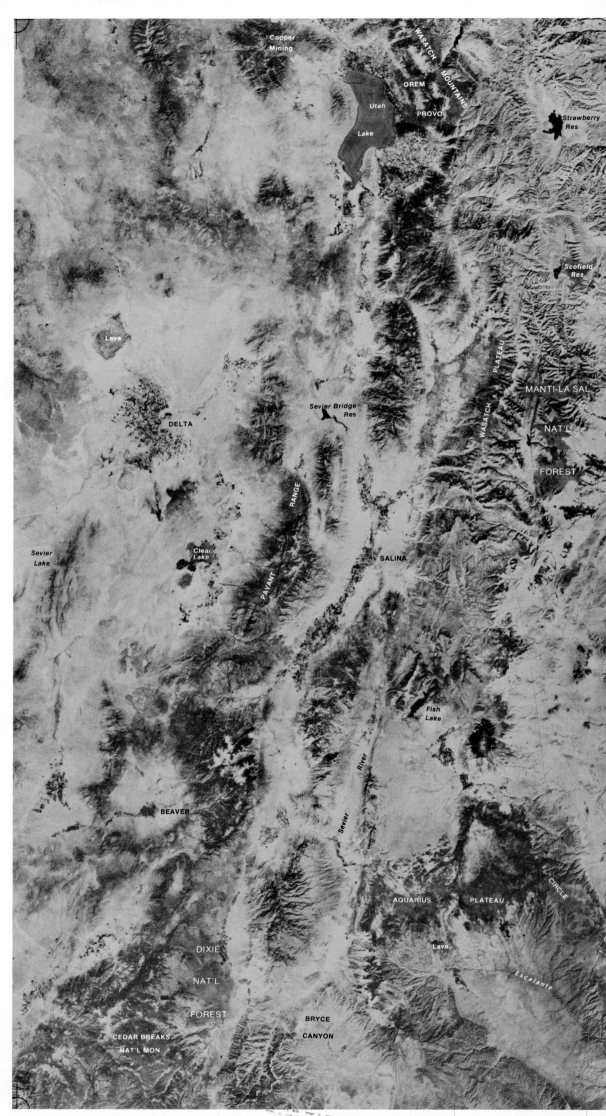

40

The **Grand Canyon,** with its mile-deep gorge and its precipitous terrain, was discovered in 1541 by one of Coronado's men. This colossal chasm, carved during many millions of years by the extraordinary **Colorado River,** reveals in its sides a veritable cross-section of all those eons, right down to the lowest (and oldest) rocks. Over this vast period of time the river has stayed in the same place while the surrounding terrain slowly rose. The erosion is accomplished by wind, frost, plants and animals, but mostly by the silt which flows in the waters. Every day the river carries about half a million tons of this silt at speeds up to 20 miles per hour.

In the northeastern corner of this photo-map is the four-cornered intersection of Colorado, New Mexico, Arizona and Utah. This is the only point in the United States where four states meet.

The **Black-Mesa** lies across the northeast corner of Arizona. Part of the Hopi-Navajo Indian Reservation, the **Black Mesa** is regarded as sacred by the Hopi. Proposals to stripmine and burn the coal found on the mesa are opposed by both environmental and religious groups.

San Francisco Mountain, just north of **Flagstaff,** is the highest point in Arizona, at nearly 13,000 feet. In its canyons are several pueblo ruins.

Sunset Crater National Monument is one of several craters found in Arizona. Probably the most famous is at **Meteor Mountain,** visible about 20 miles west of **Winslow.** Here, thousands of years ago, a great meteorite buried itself in the earth with what must have been a catastrophic explosion. The crater is some 4,000 feet across and the vertical walls about 600 feet high. The body of the meteorite, if any remains, is far below the surface.

Canyon de Chelly National Monument is visible just below the **Chuska Mountains.** The sheer walls of this canyon contain a great many cliff pueblos, including the famous White Horse. The area is a Navajo Indian Reservation.

The **Painted Desert** is named for the varieties of colored stone which make up the landscape. To the east of the **Painted Desert** are the **Hopi Buttes.**

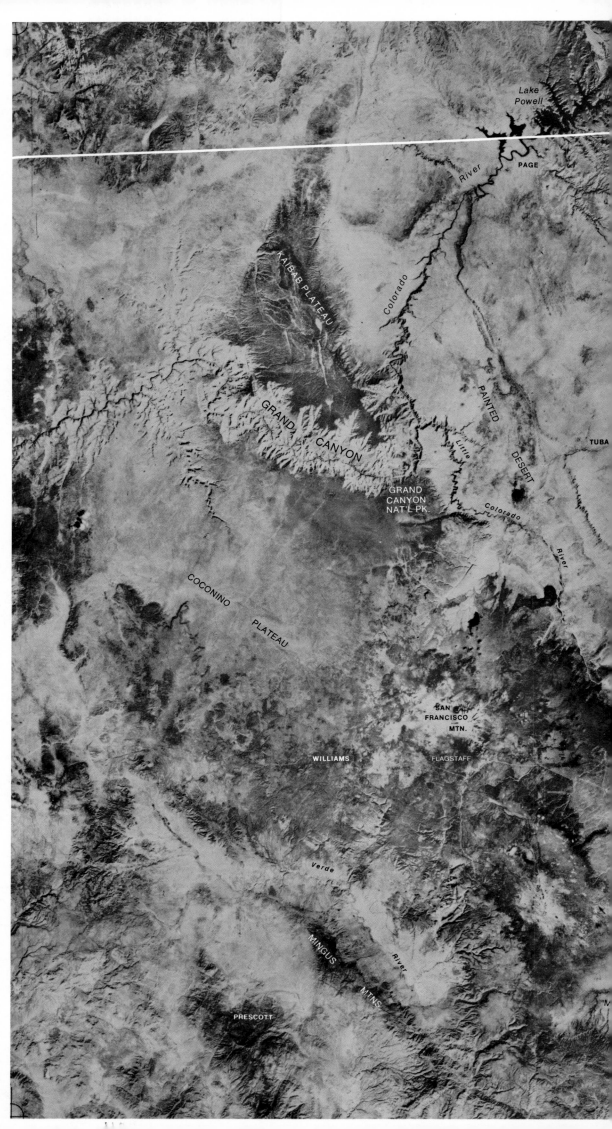

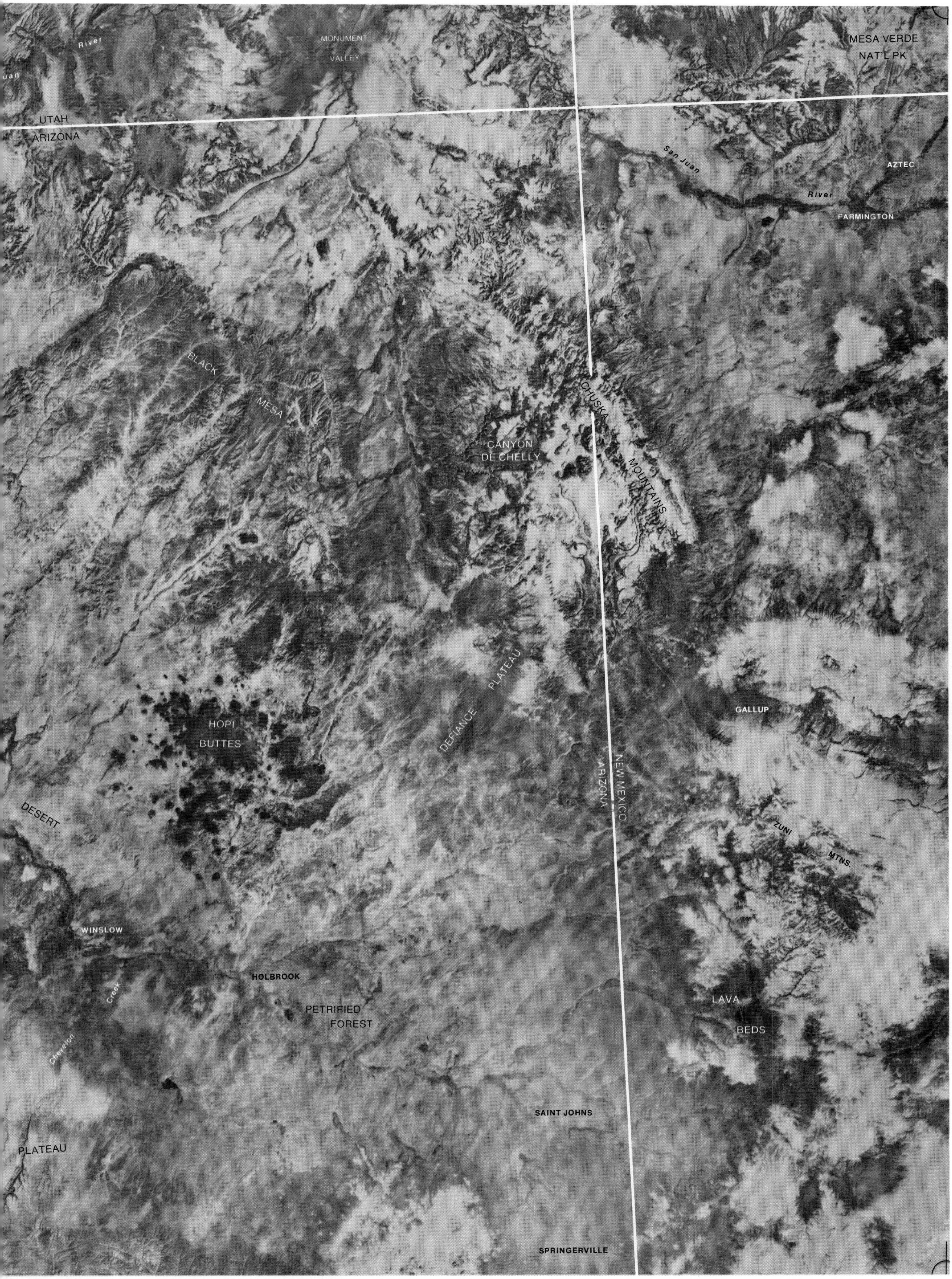

MESA VERDE
NAT'L PK

UTAH
ARIZONA

San Juan

AZTEC

River

FARMINGTON

MONUMENT
VALLEY

BLACK

MESA

CANYON
DE CHELLY

CHUSKA

MOUNTAINS

PLATEAU

GALLUP

DEFIANCE

HOPI
BUTTES

NEW MEXICO

ARIZONA

DESERT

ZUNI

MTNS.

WINSLOW

HOLBROOK

LAVA

PETRIFIED
FOREST

BEDS

Creek

Chevlon

SAINT JOHNS

PLATEAU

SPRINGERVILLE

42

The land in this photo-map shows extensive volcanic and orogenic activity. The region is also rich in precious metals including gold and copper. Heavy, precious metals are often forced to the surface during extreme geologic disturbance.

The scars of mining are visible on the photo-map. In the hills west of the **Tucson Mountains** and on the eastern slopes of the **Sierrita Mountains** can be seen the whitish scars of copper mines. Another large open-pit copper mine lies just south of **Ajo,** Arizona. Gold, silver, lead, and zinc are also mined in the area covered by this photo-map.

The **Superstition Mountains** were and still are shunned by natives as the dwelling place of evil spirits. Somewhere in these mountains is the famous Lost Dutchman Mine.

From time immemorial, turquoise has been the most highly esteemed gemstone among southwest Indians. It is found only in a handfull of places. Mines in the **Burro Mountains** are a principal source, and have been nearly exhausted. That is one reason turquoise has risen in price during the last few years.

The **San Pedro River** valley was probably the route used by Coronado in his search for the legendary seven Cities of Cibola.

Near **Casa Grande** is a pueblo built perhaps 1,000 years ago, located at the bend in the **Gila River** (about 2 in. southeast of **Phoenix**).

In 1871 a Lieutenant Cushing and nearly all of his cavalry detachment were ambushed and destroyed by Cochise in the **Whetstone Mountains.** Cochise was an extremely clever defender of Indian freedom, and maintained a stronghold in the mountainous ridge just south and west of **Wilcox Plaza.** His canyon had a mouth so narrow that a man or two could defend it against an army.

The agriculture in the **Phoenix** vicinity is the result of irrigation. Cattle, dairy products, cotton and vegetables are produced. Archeological evidence shows that this region was first irrigated by an ancient but highly technical people known as the Hohokams. During the period from about 300 B.C. to 1100 A.D., these people irrigated thousands of acres with water from the **Gila** and **Salt Rivers.**

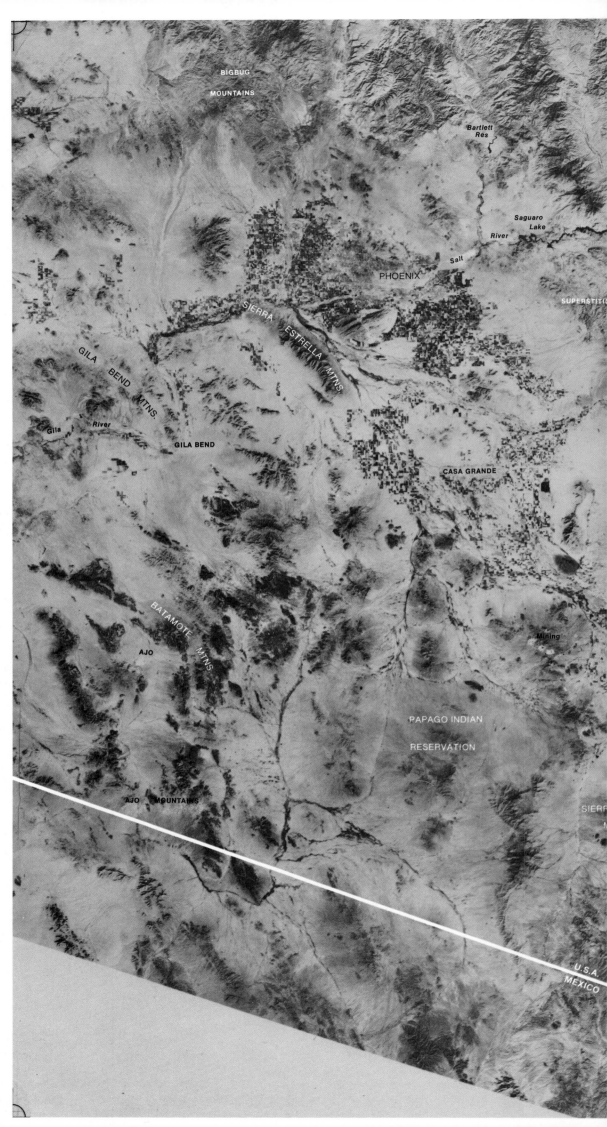

McNARY

BALD
PEAK

GLOBE

San Carlos
Lake

San Francisco

River

NEW MEXICO

ARIZONA

Gila

River

SILVER
CITY

THATCHER

Salt

River

Gila

River

San

Pedro

River

Gila

River

BURRO MTNS

BOWIE

San Simon

TUCSON

Wilcox

Playa

Creek

BENSON

CHIRICAHUA MTNS

WHETSTONE MTNS

TOMBSTONE

BISBEE

DOUGLAS

ARIZONA

SONORA

AGUA PRIETA

OGALES

Careful viewing of this photo-map reveals a contrast between the agricultural patterns north and south of the **Missouri River.** The river's present course basically follows the edge of the gigantic continental ice sheet which covered the area to the north before the glaciers receded about ten thousand years ago. As a result of glaciation, the soils to the north of the **Missouri** were enriched.

Limited moisture (about 15 inches of precipitation a year) forces most cropland to be focused near rivers for the irrigation water they provide.

Long, thin agricultural fields can be seen in the northeast portion of this photo-map. Strip-cropping, or the alternating of strips of spring wheat with fallow fields, is an attempt to make maximum use of limited rainfall.

The spring wheat belt exten northwestward into Canada. T reason for this is, of course climate. The winters of th northern Great Plains are t severe for a wheat crop plante

the fall to survive. A distinc-
n in agricultural field patterns
visible on this photo-map
rth and south of the interna-
nal border. The graphic bor-
line has been removed west

of the **Turtle Mountains** and
north of **Medicine Lake** to enable
better viewing of this distinction. A more impressive example
of this phenomenon is provided
with photo-map pp. 32-33.

The forest-clad **Black Hills** contrast darkly against the surrounding lighter grasslands. Western Yellow Pine and Douglas Fir cloak the hills which rise 4,000 feet as the eroded remnants of an uplifted dome geologically related to the Rocky Mountains. The **Black Hills** resulted as a dome of ancient rock pushed up younger sedimentary rock which eroded into rings of hog backs.

The **Devils Tower,** to the northwest of the **Black Hills,** is composed of volcanic rock.

The state of South Dakota leads the U.S. in gold output, due almost entirely to the production of the famous Homestake Mine, located at **Lead** in the northern **Black Hills.**

The **Mount Rushmore** National Memorial is in the eastern Black Hills. Sixty-foot-high heads of four United States Presidents (Washington, Lincoln, Jefferson, and T. Roosevelt) are carved into the mountain. Just to the southwest, the Crazy Horse Memorial, over 500 feet high, is being carved into Thunderhead Mountain.

The whitish-colored patch in the southeastern corner of this photo-map is the **Badlands** National Monument. The soft, sedimentary rocks have been severely eroded by the **White River** and its tributaries into an extremely rugged landscape of sharp ridges and steep-sided canyons.

Wounded Knee, south of the **Badlands,** is the site of the last major conflict between the U.S. Army and the Sioux Indians. An encampment of Indian men, women, and children was massacred here in 1890.

Agriculture in this area includes cattle and sheep ranching and the growing of spring and winter wheat and barley. This portion of the Great Plains is between the spring wheat region to the north and the winter wheat area of the warmer southern plains.

Most of this area is grazing land of native grasses including western wheatgrass and needlegrass. Irrigated agriculture is evident in some of the valleys and lowlands. Higher elevations are forested with stands of Ponderosa Pine and Western Red Cedar.

MONTANA

NORTH DAKOTA
SOUTH DAKOTA

Bowman
Haley
Res.

LEMMON

Shadehill
Res.

Grand River

River

Little

Missouri

River

Moreau

River

DUPREE

Belle
Fourche
Res.

Cheyenne River

L'S
ER

S.D.
WYO

LEAD

Mining

BLACK

HILLS

MT
RUSHMORE

RAPID CITY

Beaver

Creek

BADLANDS

White River

Angostura
Res.

enne

River

WOUNDED KNEE

The Oregon Trail and the Morman Trail followed the **North Platte River.** The pioneers left the **North Platt** near the **Pathfinder Reservoir** and followed the **Sweetwater River** (see photo-map pp. 36-37) westward.

Between **Cheyenne** and **Laramie** is the Gangplank. This is one of the few natural ramps offering a gradual grade from the Great Plains to the Rocky Mountain highlands. The Union Pacific Railroad chose this route for the trans-continental railway, rather than cross the **Front Range** to the south or the **Laramie Range** to the north. The east-west drainage patterns, visible on this photo-map, contrast with the north-south drainage patterns of the **Front Range,** indicating the erosion that has taken place to form the Gangplank.

The Union Pacific Railroad runs through **Cheyenne** and **Laramie,** then curves northwest, around the **Medicine Bow Mountains,** and through **Rawlins,** Wyoming.

The eastern edge of this photo-map is dominated by complex sand dunes and ridges rising several hundred feet and separated by numerous small basins. This is the largest area of sand dunes in the nation. The abundant native grasses, and the accumulation of water in the many depressions provide feed and water for the livestock raised on the large ranches which dominate the **Sand Hills.** The dunes were formed by winds during a time when this region was almost void of vegetation.

Areas of irrigated agriculture on this photo-map contrast with those areas where irrigation water is not available. Annual precipitation in the cultivated portions of this photo-map is normally under 10 inches. The valley flood plains are dark with intense cultivation, including corn and sugar beets. Elsewhere the dry range prevails.

The heavy agriculture area near **Greeley** requires more water than is locally available. Water is actually transported from the wetter slopes on the western side of the mountains. A tunnel nine feet in diameter and thirteen miles long was cut through the mountains to transport water to the dry plains. The tunnel is 4,000 feet below the **Continental Divide.**

WYOMING

S.D.

NEBR.

PINE RIDGE

CHADRON

LUSK

NEBRASKA NAT'L FOREST

Niobrara River

Niobrara River

Snake River

SAND

HILLS

ALLIANCE

TORRINGTON

Lake
Minatare

LAND

SCOTTSBLUFF

WILDCAT HILLS

North Platte River

Lake
McConaughy

KIMBALL

Lodgepole Creek

CHEYENNE

NEBR.
COLO.

South Platte River

Sterling
Res

STERLING

HOLYOKE

T COLLINS

GREELEY

Riverside
Res.

Circular
Irrigation

WRAY

The sharp contrast between the flat Great Plains and the rugged Rocky Mountains remains an enigma to geologists. The photo-map shows very clearly this contrast in topography west of **Denver** and west of **Fort Collins** (see photo-map pp. 48-49). A currently popular geologic theory known as plate tectonics suggests that the North American Continent (or continental plate) separated here along a north-south seam. The continent then reunited and this portion of the Rockies was formed during the collision. The collision began about 70 million years ago.

The high plains in the right portion of this photo-map are at an elevation of about 6,000 feet. This is unusually high for such a flat area. The natural vegetation here is bluestem and sandsage in the east and the shorter buffalo grass along the western edge of the plains.

A continuous pattern of cultivated fields can be seen along the eastern edge of this photo-map. This pattern disappears to the west where less rainfall dictates cattle ranching and other dry range agriculture. The exception is along the rivers, where irrigation enables production of dairy products and sugar beets.

The major Colorado cities, usually associated with the Rocky Mountains, actually are located several miles out on the plains. **Denver, Colorado Springs,** and **Pueblo** lie in a north-south line on the plains below the mountains. **Pike's Peak** presents a scenic backdrop to **Colorado Springs.**

Leadville, at an elevation of almost two miles, is one of the highest cities in the United States. Founded in 1877 during a lead and silver boom, **Leadville** was once the second largest city in Colorado.

Several great rivers of North America originate in the mountains on the western half of this photo-map: The **Colorado,** the **North** and **South Platte** (see also photo-map pp. 48-49), the **Arkansas,** and the **Rio Grande.**

The **San Luis Valley,** an example of a large intermontane valley in the Southern Rockies, has several craters or cinder cones in its southern part. The **Rio Grande** flows south from here.

DENVER

ENGLEWOOD

LIMON

Creek

Big Sandy

Arikaree

River

South Fork Republican River

Bonny
Res

Big Sandy Creek

PIKES
PEAK

COLORADO
SPRINGS

CRIPPLE CREEK

Great
Plains
Res.

CANON CITY

Mining

Lake
Meredith

PUEBLO

Arkansas River

Arkansas River

John Martin
Res

WET

MTNS

River

Huerfano

Butte River

CRISTO

WALSENBURG

Two

SPRINGFIELD

MOUNTAINS

River

Purgatoire

River

TRINIDAD

COLO.

N. MEX.

OKLA.

The **Continental Divide** crosses the northwest corner of this photo-map. In this region water to the east of the divide flows to the Gulf of Mexico via the **Rio Grande.** Water to the west flows to the Gulf of California via the Colorado River.

The region along the eastern edge of this photo-map (and continuing in photo-map pp. 64-65) is one of the most heavily irrigated areas in the Southwest. Grains and cotton are grown here.

The progress of intensive crop agriculture into eastern New Mexico in the early 1930's was discouraged by the dry years which resulted in the Dust Bowl. Wind erosion severely eroded the topsoil sending towering clouds of dust to the states further east.

In this region where water is of vital importance, a photo-map can play an interesting role. The graphic borderline between Texas and New Mexico has been removed, south of **Clayton.** The state borderline is still visible because of differences in irrigation.

Large ranches dominate eastern New Mexico. Most of the range is native grassland and shrub. In higher elevations some pinyon-juniper woodlands are encountered. Cattle and sheep are grazed, but large acreages are required to support a few animals since the rainfall of only 10 to 15 inches each year provides somewhat meager vegetation. Where water for irrigation is available from the rivers or from wells in the Staked Plains (**Llano Estacado**) (also see photo-map pp. 64-65) in the east, cotton, vegetables and cantaloupes are produced. Wheat is an important crop in the smoother uplands.

The **Sandia Mountains** overlook **Albuquerque,** which together with **Los Alamos** to the north, is the home of many of the nation's most brilliant and affluent scientists. There are two Albuquerques. Spanish Old Town began in 1598. An enclosed plaza formerly served as a corral at night. In the 1880's the railroads arrived and the new town began to grow. Albuquerque, the site of the University of New Mexico, now functions as a commercial and banking center, especially for the sheep and wool industries.

SANGRE DE CRISTO MTNS

RATON

OKLAHOMA

NEW MEXICO

CLAYTON

TURKEY
MOUNTAIN

LLANO

LAS VEGAS

NEW MEXICO

TEXAS

Canadian

Conchas
Res.

River

MESCALERO

TUCUMCARI

ESTACADO

RIDGE

SANTA ROSA

Alamogordo Res

VAUGHN

CLOVIS

River

PORTALES

NCOLN

Pecos

NAT'L

FOREST

54

Franklin Mountain north of **El Paso** is considered to be the southernmost peak of the Rocky Mountains. The lava beds to the west are evidence of the prehistoric volcanic activity in this area.

El Camino Real, the first Spanish highway on the continent, crosses the **Rio Grande** at **El Paso.**

The small town of **Columbus,** only a few miles from the U.S. border, was the scene of an armed raid by General Pancho Villa in 1916. The incident nearly led to a war between the two countries. Today there is a monument to General Villa in **Columbus.**

The **Pecos River,** near the eastern edge of this photo-map, indicates that this region is "west of the Pecos," where the fast guns of western lore abounded.

The Goodnight Loving Trail ran north-south, almost parallel to the **Pecos River** and was a prominent avenue of transporting longhorn cattle from the Texas range westward and northward.

This remains cattle country. Ranches average 25,000 acres in this dry, rugged region. Yearly rainfall is ten inches or less in most of this area.

Native grasses dominate the vegetation but provide only sparse feed. About 150 acres of range are required to feed a single steer. A few ribbons of darker irrigated floodplains along the infrequent streams produce cotton and vegetables.

The extensive subterranean caves of the **Carlsbad Caverns** are located in southeastern New Mexico at the right center of this photo-map.

The **Carlsbad** region is by far the greatest potash producing area of the United States. Potash is an extremely important fertilizer and is also used in several types of manufacturing.

The oil field associated with the west Texas plains covers the eastern edge of this photo-map including southeastern New Mexico.

The **White Sands National Monument** contains many square miles of white gypsum sand dunes. The area to the north is a testing ground for rockets and guided missiles.

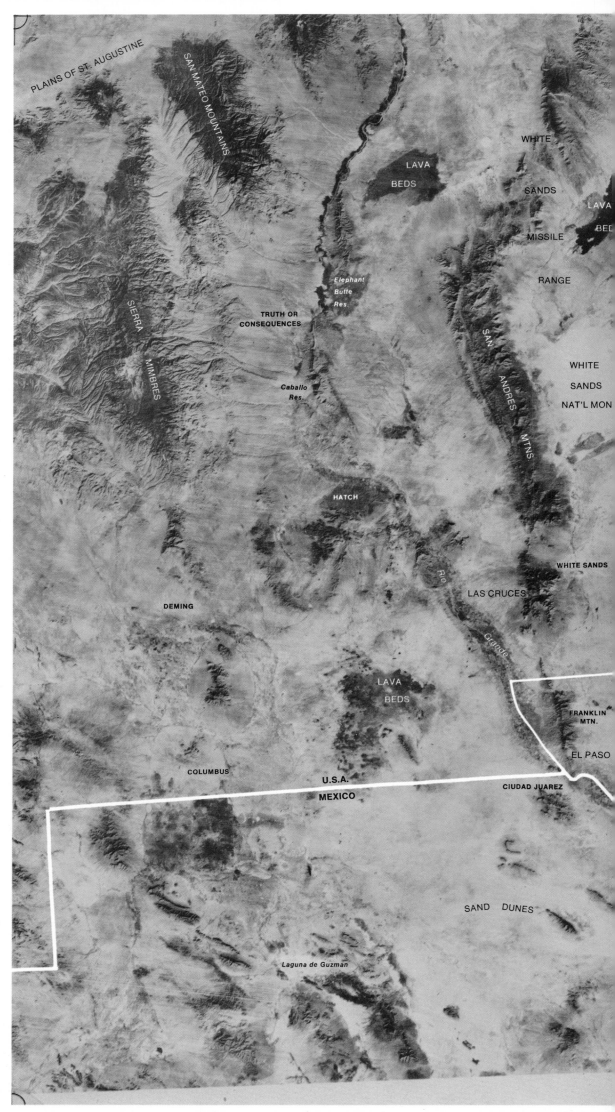

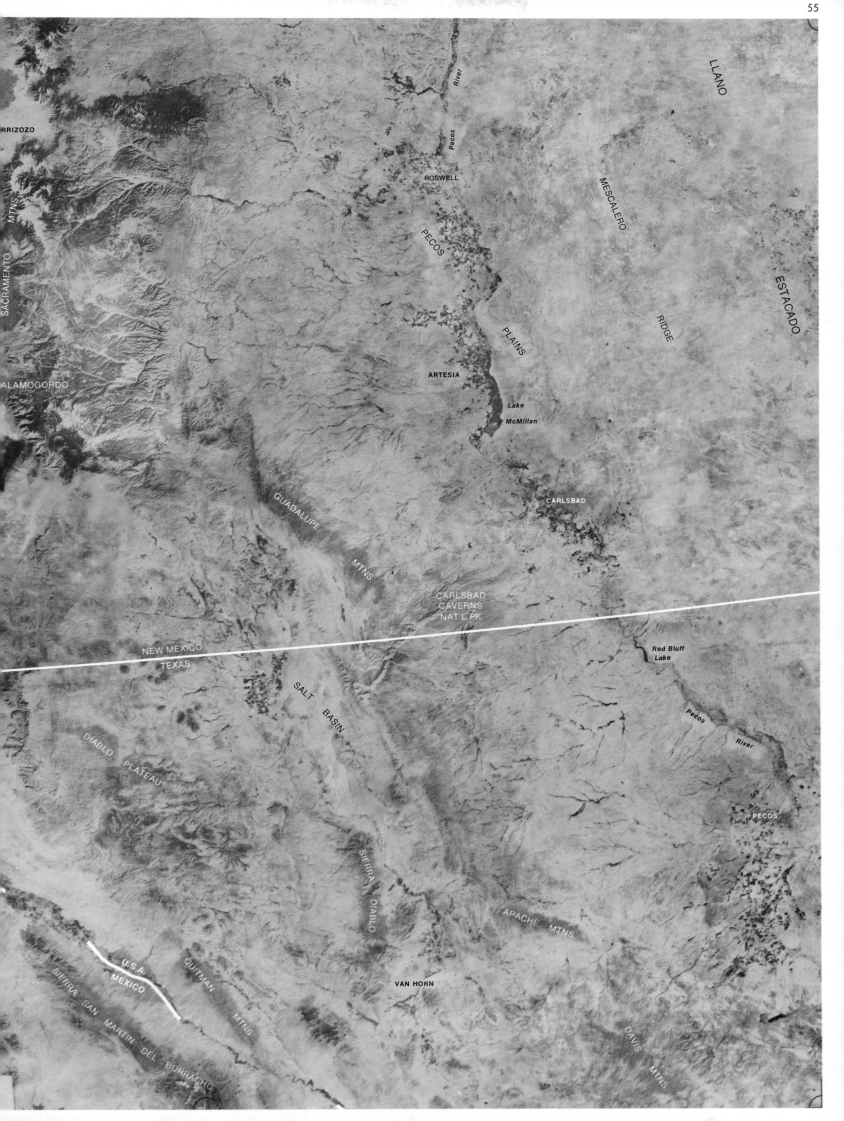

LLANO

ESTACADO

MESCALERO

RIDGE

River

Pecos

ROSWELL

PECOS

PLAINS

ARTESIA

Lake
McMillan

CARLSBAD

RRIZOZO

SACRAMENTO

MTNS.

ALAMOGORDO

GUADALUPE

MTNS.

CARLSBAD
CAVERNS
NAT'L PK.

Red Bluff
Lake

NEW MEXICO
TEXAS

SALT

BASIN

Pecos

River

DIABLO

PLATEAU

PECOS

SIERRA

DIABLO

APACHE MTNS.

U.S.A.
MEXICO

QUITMAN

VAN HORN

SIERRA SAN MARTIN DEL BORRACHO

MTNS.

DAVIS

MTNS.

PORTAGE
LA PRAIRIE

Assiniboine

River

BRANDON

Assiniboine

River

Souris

River

River

PEMBINA HILLS

Pelican Lake

Pembina

Whitewater
Lake

Souris

River

Rush
Lake

CANADA

U.S.A.

PEMBINA HILLS

Souris

TURTLE MTS.

Dry
Lake

RUGBY

Devils
Lake

Sheyenne

River

River

MINOT

Souris

River

NEW
ROCKFORD

James

River

James

River

Horsehead
Lake

JAMESTOWN

The northward projection of the United States border into the **Lake of the Woods** created a remote bit of the U.S.A. called the Northwest Angle.

The topography of the region in this photo-map was severely influenced by tremendous continental glaciers, thousands of feet thick, which covered the area until about 10,000 years ago. **Lake of the Woods** and **Upper** and **Lower Red Lake** are especially large examples of Minnesota's ten thousand lakes. They are water-filled depressions left by the ice as it melted and retreated northward.

Minnesota's largest state park, covering some 32,000 acres, is near **Bemidji.** Over 150 lakes lie within the park, including **Lake Itasca,** the source of the **Mississippi River.**

South of the **Turtle Mountains,** near the small town of **Rugby,** North Dakota, is the geographical center of the North American continent.

WINNIPEG

Rat

River

Roseau

River

ONTARIO
MANITOBA

Whitemouth Lake

Lake of the Woods

WARROAD

Rainy   River

MANITOBA

MINNESOTA

AKOTA

Thief Lake

AGASSIZ
NWR

Mud
Lake

Upper Red Lake

GRAFTON

Lower Red Lake

THIEF RIVER
FALLS

Red   Lake   River

River

GRAND
FORKS

Red   Lake   River

Red

MINN.
N.D.

BEMIDJI

Mississippi   River

Lake
Itasca

Red

River

bula

DETROIT
LAKES

FARGO

LLEY CITY

The area covered by this photo-map represents portions of the Great Plains and the Central Lowlands. The division between these geologic provinces is apparent just west of **Elm Lake** and running parallel with the **James River.** A north-south trending ridge abruptly separates the Black Prairie lowlands to the east from the Missouri Plateau section of the Great Plains.

The **Missouri River** is the approximate dividing line between the glaciated area to the northeast and the area to the southwest which was not covered by the continental ice sheets. The glacial epoch, which ended about ten thousand years ago, still influences the use of the land. Note the different agricultural patterns north and south of the **Missouri River.** The soils which were leveled and enriched by glaciation are heavily cultivated. The unglaciated soils to the southwest are still mostly in native grasses and are more associated with ranching activities.

The pronounced distinction between the topography east and west of the **Missouri River** in South Dakota prompted early pioneers in the region to describe their location as east or west of the river. The two nearly equal sections of the state, separated by the **Missouri,** differed considerably in their history and growth.

The **Missouri River** has been extensively dammed throughout most of its course across the plains, creating elongated reservoirs like **Lake Oahe** and **Lake Sharp.**

The influence of the continental ice sheets on the landscape of this region is readily seen in satellite photography. The clusters of small lakes and ponds in the eastern portion of this photo-map are water-filled depressions left by receding glaciers. Most of the rivers, like the **James** and the **Big Sioux,** drain north to south as a result of glacial action.

The right half of this photo-map represents the most western limits of the Corn Belt. **Sioux Falls,** South Dakota serves as a Tri-State commercial and industrial center for this Corn Belt region of South Dakota, Minnesota and Iowa.

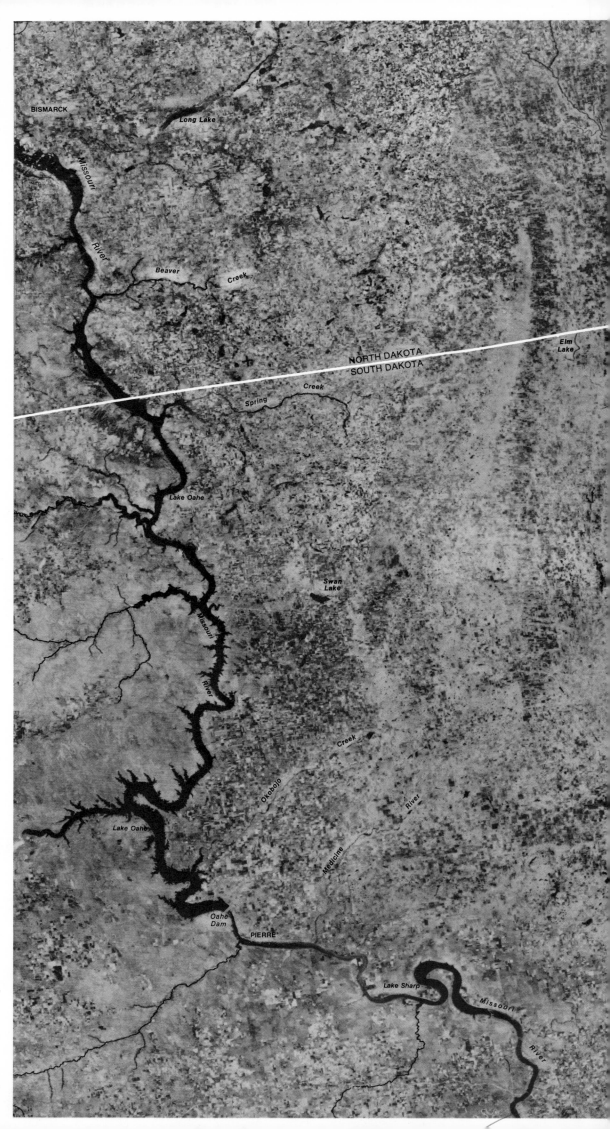

Sheyenne River

Otter
Tail
Lake

WAHPETON

Lake
Miltona

Lake
Osakis

N.D.

S.D.

River

Lake
Minnewaska

Lake Traverse

Mud Lake
Res.

Dry
Wood
Lake

Big Stone
Lake

APPLETON

Waubay
Lake

Lac Qui Parle
Lake

RDEEN

Minnesota

River

MINNESOTA

SOUTH DAKOTA

Lake
Poinsett

MARSHALL

Lake
Byron

James

River

Thompson
Lake

HURON

PIPESTONE

River

Sioux

Madison
Lake

Big

WORTHINGTON

James

River

MITCHELL

MINN.

SIOUX FALLS

IOWA

The Great Plains appear to be level but are actually sloped downward to the east. The surface at the western margin of this picture is about 4,000 feet above sea level but at the eastern margin it has dropped to around 1,500 feet. The slope of the plains downward from the base of the Rocky Mountains is largely due to the mountains being eroded away with the debris washing eastward onto the plains.

River drainage patterns comply with the landscape. The flat, gently sloping land of the plains gives rise to the parallel and dendritic river and stream courses such as the numerous tributaries of the **Loup River.**

The **Sand Hills** are thought to be made up of sand from dry stream channels, blown by the wind to this upland area.

During much of the mid-nineteenth century the Great Plains were known as the Great American Desert. Zebulon Pike coined this term in his 1806 report of his exploration. The Great Plains suffered from such unfair estimates of their ultimate potential. Later, would-be-developers of the region just as unfairly oversold this rather sparsely-watered region as an agricultural Eden.

The **Platte River** ambles across the plains from the Rockies, carrying much sand and gravel. The sprawl of the **Platte** across its wide, gravelly bed had caused it to be described as a mile wide and a foot deep.

Major Pioneer trails, such as the Mormon Trail and the Oregon Trail, paralleled the **North Platte River.**

From these pictures, taken over 500 miles in space, one can see that the **White River** is aptly named. Light colored silt eroded into streams from the Badlands to the west (photo-map pp. 46-47) is the apparent source of the whitish color of the river.

Extensive irrigation and soil conservation techniques have been utilized to transform this region into an agriculturally productive land. Cattle, spring wheat, and sorghums are major products in this area. Irrigation, such as along the **Platte River,** enables production of sugar beets and dairy goods.

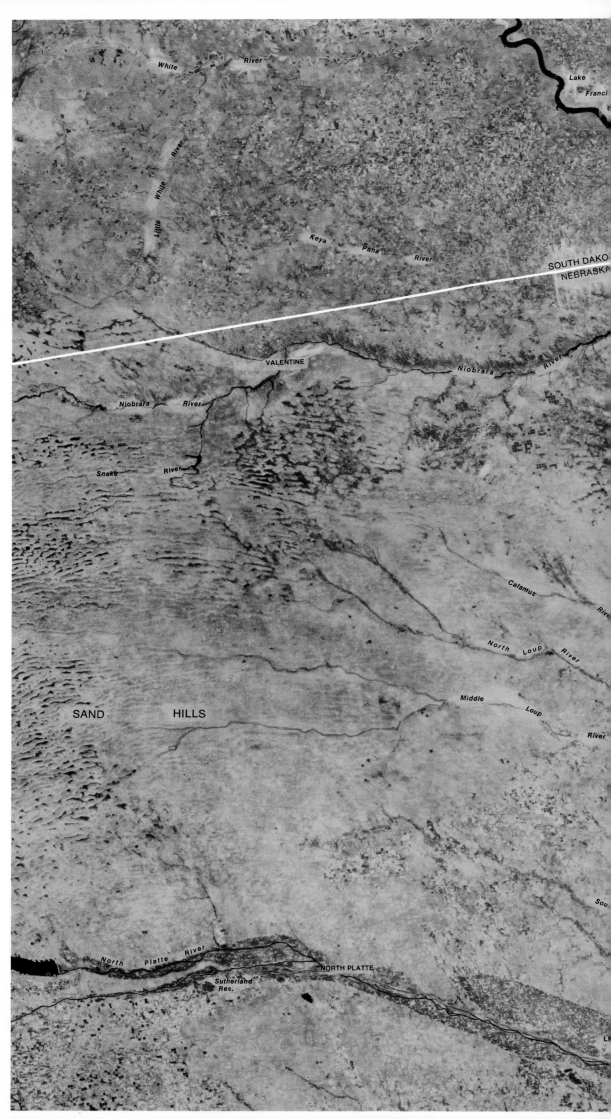

Lake
Andes

James *River*

Big *Sioux* *River*

Floyd *River*

LE MARS

YANKTON

S.D.
IOWA

Missouri *River*

Lewis and
Clark Lake

SIOUX
CITY

rcular

Irrigation

O'NEILL

IOWA
NEBR.

Elkhorn

River

NORFOLK

Beaver

Creek

River

Platte

FREMONT

COLUMBUS

Sherman
Res.

Loup *River*

LINCOLN

Big

oup

River

GRAND ISLAND

Platte *River*

Blue

River

KEARNEY

HASTINGS

BEATRICE

62

The section of central Kansas dominating this photo-map consists of the relatively dry Great Plains to the west and the wetter prairie region of the Central Lowlands east of **Salina.** Rainfall averages from about 15 inches in the west up to 30 inches annually in the east.

The contrasting tones and patterns on the landscape in the western portion of this photo-map indicate three different types of agricultural land use:

1. Intermixed areas of highly contrasting dark and light fields, often located along rivers such as the **Republican** and **Frenchman Creek,** are irrigated for the cultivation of corn, sugar beets, alfalfa and grain sorghum.

2. The more subdued contrasts which still exhibit an obvious field pattern (sometimes very elongated fields such as those north of the **Arkansas River** in the southwestern corner of this photo-map) indicate a lower intensity of cultivation—usually dry-farmed wheat.

3. Non-cropped, but often grazed areas are of a medium shade. Sometimes these are sand dunes which are brought under irrigation (such as those southwest of **Garden City**) by pumping ground water and sprinkling it from a pipe moving on wheels with a well as a central pivot. This causes the curious, dark, circular patterns usually one half a mile in diameter.

The Great Plains are characterized by a flat to rolling topography with few trees except along the rivers.

Manmade reservoirs such as **Waconda Reservoir** and **Wilson Reservoir** dot this region. There are also several natural depressions which collect water during wet periods. **Cheyenne Bottoms,** in the center of the photo-map, is one of these.

Pioneer and cattle trails crisscrossed Kansas. Pioneer wagons following the Santa Fe Trail closely paralleled the course of the **Arkansas River** across central and western Kansas. Overland cattle trails from the Texas rangelands to the south were the only access ranchers had to Kansas' eastbound railroads.

Near **Mankato,** in the northeastern part of this photo-map, is the geographical center of the

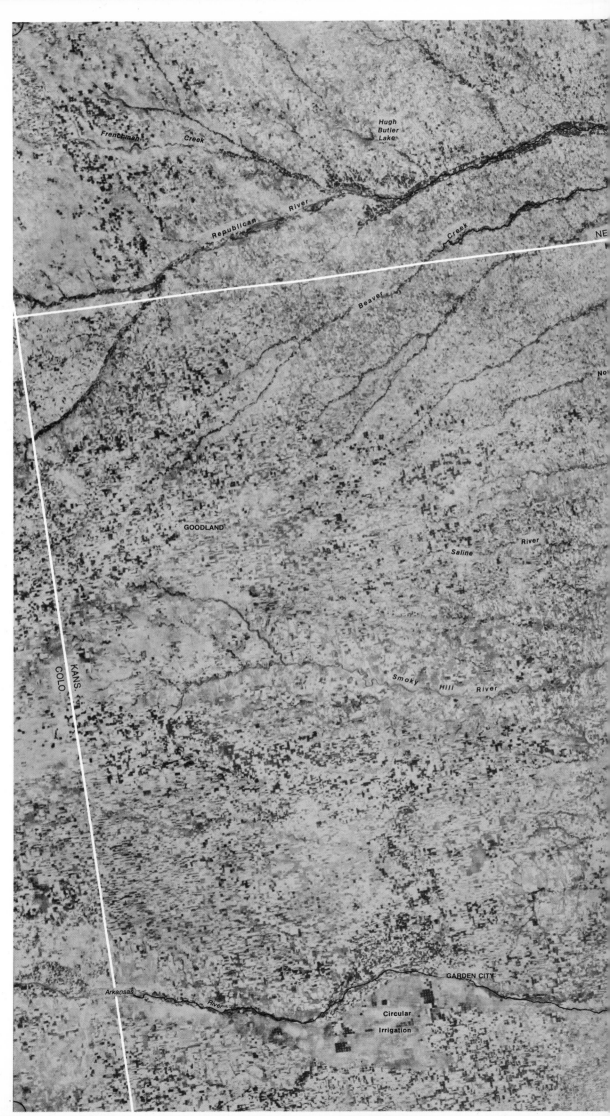

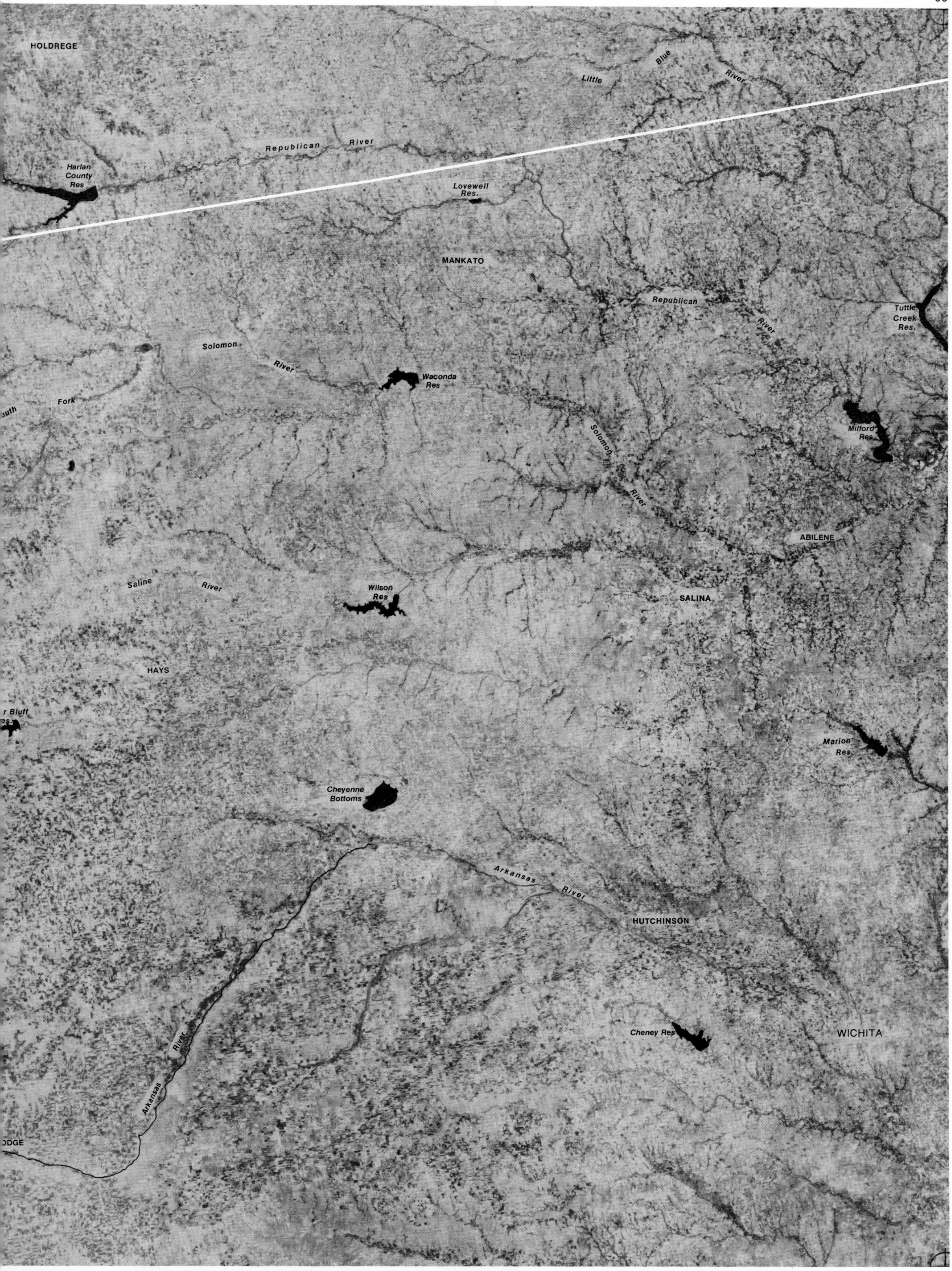

63

HOLDREGE

Little

Blue

River

Republican   River

Harlan
County
Res.

Lovewell
Res.

MANKATO

Republican

River

Tuttle
Creek
Res.

Solomon

River

Waconda
Res

Solomon

River

Milford
Res.

South

Fork

ABILENE

Saline   River

Wilson
Res.

SALINA

HAYS

r Bluff
es.

Marion
Res.

Cheyenne
Bottoms

Arkansas   River

HUTCHINSON

Arkansas   River

Cheney Res.

WICHITA

DODGE

Rolling topography characterizes the Texas, Oklahoma and Kansas landscape shown in this photo-map. The 100th meridian stretches from north to south across the photo-map forming part of the Texas-Oklahoma border. This meridian is the approximate dividing line between the humid eastern United States and the arid lands to the west.

Annual rainfall in the region pictured increases from about 15 inches in the west to around 35 inches in the east. Since 20 inches is generally presumed to be the approximate dividing line between irrigated and non-irrigated agriculture, irrigation is practiced mostly in the western portion of this photo-map.

The significant increase in rainfall to the east means that natural vegetation changes accordingly. Prairie grasses in the west are replaced by decidous woodlands in the east. These wooded areas are depicted in the darker tones on the photo-map in the regions drained by the **Cimarron, Canadian** and **Washita Rivers.**

Nearly half the area on this photo-map is rangeland, where the grazing of cattle on native grasses is significant.

Though precipitation on the Great Plains averages about fifteen inches a year, this amount fluctuates widely from year to year. A series of wet years in the western plains may tempt farmers to strip the soils of protective grass cover to plant row crops. This happened in the early 1930's, but then a series of dry years ensued. Millions of acres of topsoil were blown from these plains to the South and Midwest during the Dust Bowl of the mid-thirties.

The **Prairie Dog Town Fork** of the **Red River** (lower center in this photo-map) was so named for the numerous prairie dog towns (groups of mounds and burrows constructed by these animals) that once dotted the short-grass plains of this region. Before the plains were settled, these dog towns ranged for miles and were populated by millions of the small rodents. Today, prairie dog towns are usually found only in the national parks and protected game refuges of the Great Plains. The dog towns of today cover only a few acres.

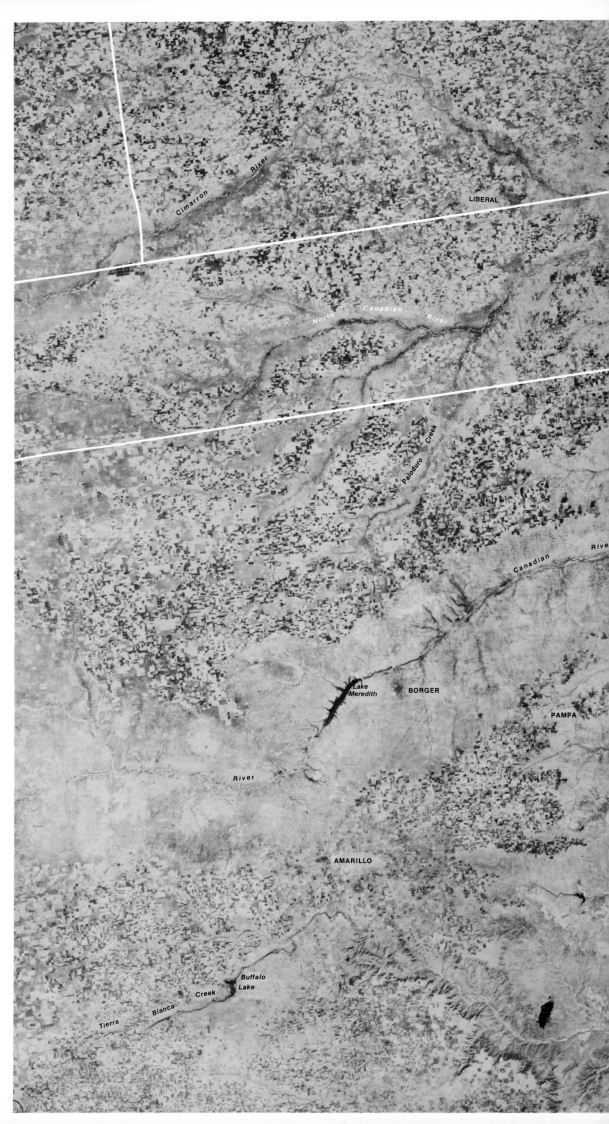

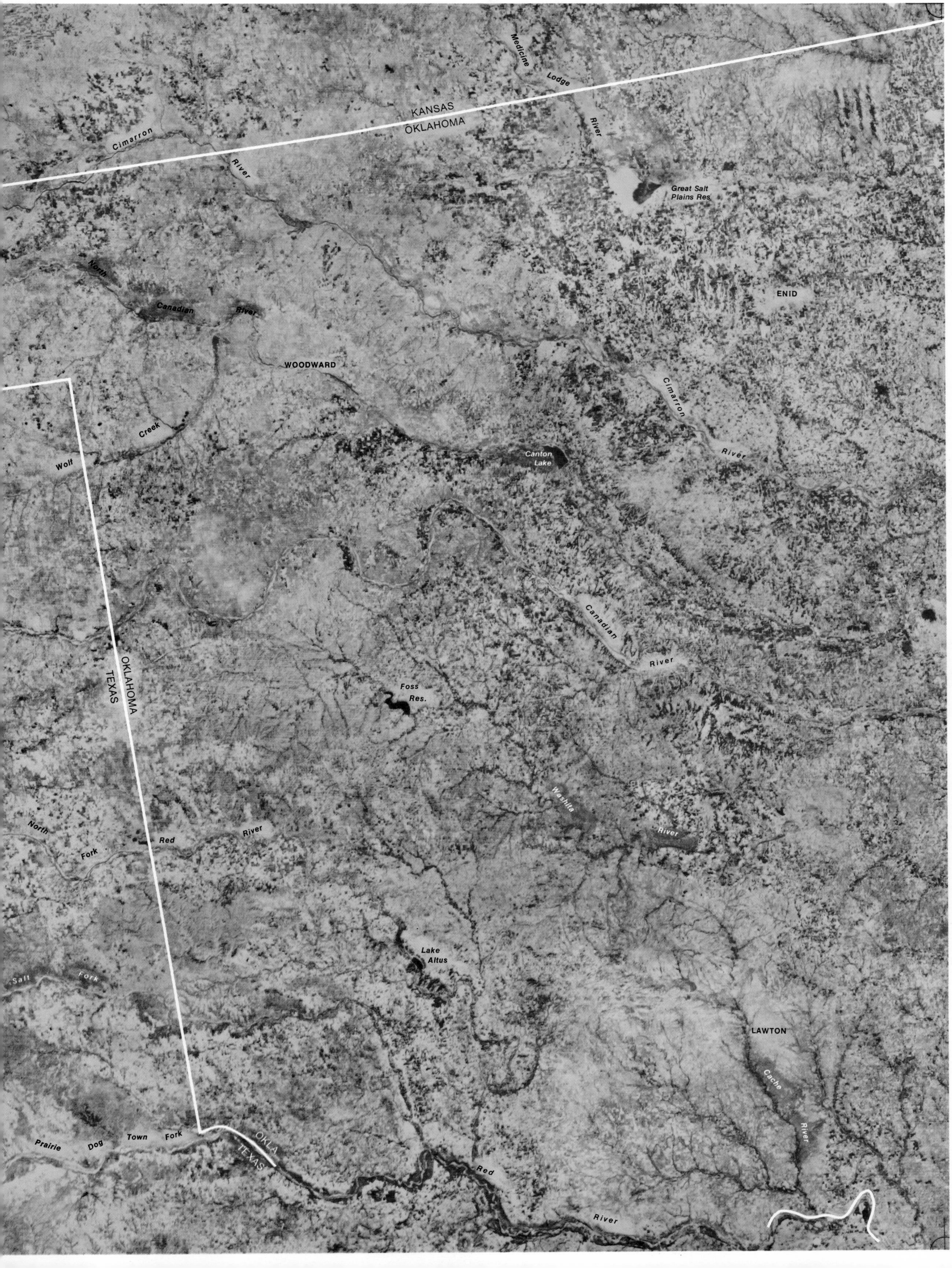

Medicine Lodge River

KANSAS
OKLAHOMA

Cimarron River

Great Salt
Plains Res

ENID

North Canadian River

WOODWARD

Creek

Wolf

Canton Lake

Cimarron River

OKLAHOMA
TEXAS

Canadian River

Foss Res.

Washita River

North Fork

Salt Fork

Red River

Lake Altus

LAWTON

Cache River

Prairie Dog Town Fork

OKLA
TEXAS

Red River

The **Llano Estacado** (Staked Plains) dominate the western portion of this photo-map. The southern high plains slope very gradually to the east, but maintain an extremely flat appearance. In fact the name, Staked Plains, is said to derive from the fact that the area was so flat and devoid of landmarks that early trails crossing it had to be clearly staked-out to keep travelers from wandering aimlessly.

The **Staked Plains** are not only flat, but hot and dry. An early explorer stated that the area was so godforsaken that it could never support human habitation. This estimation was a little severe, but until recent decades ranching and dryland wheat farming dominated the economic activities and the area was sparsely settled. Now this is a major cotton producing region. Ever-deepening wells dot the area to provide irrigation water. This water supply is rapidly being depleted, however, and may threaten the area's agricultural prosperity.

Unlike the plains to the north, margins of the rivers in this region are not cropped, but the uplands are. The rivers here have cut deep canyons, very rugged for cropland, and flow eastward over the **Caprock Escarpment** to the lower lands to the east. The canyon lands are usually left in native pasture.

Below **Lubbock** in this photo-map, irrigation of crops diminishes and the agricultural patterns reflect the change, grading from small, bright and dark fields of irrigated cotton and sorghum to the larger blocks of pasture and rangeland to the south.

In the **Lubbock** region can be seen numerous small, dark, circular features. These are depressions and are probably formed by a number of processes ranging from the solution and subsidence action of water and gravity, to blowouts caused by wind, or the remains of buffalo wallows.

The portion of this photo-map which includes **Abilene,** the **Brazos River** and **Wichita Falls** is part of the Coastal Plains province of the United States. In this photo-map, elevation increases in the Great Plains to the west (the plains begin in the vicinity of the **Caprock Escarpment**).

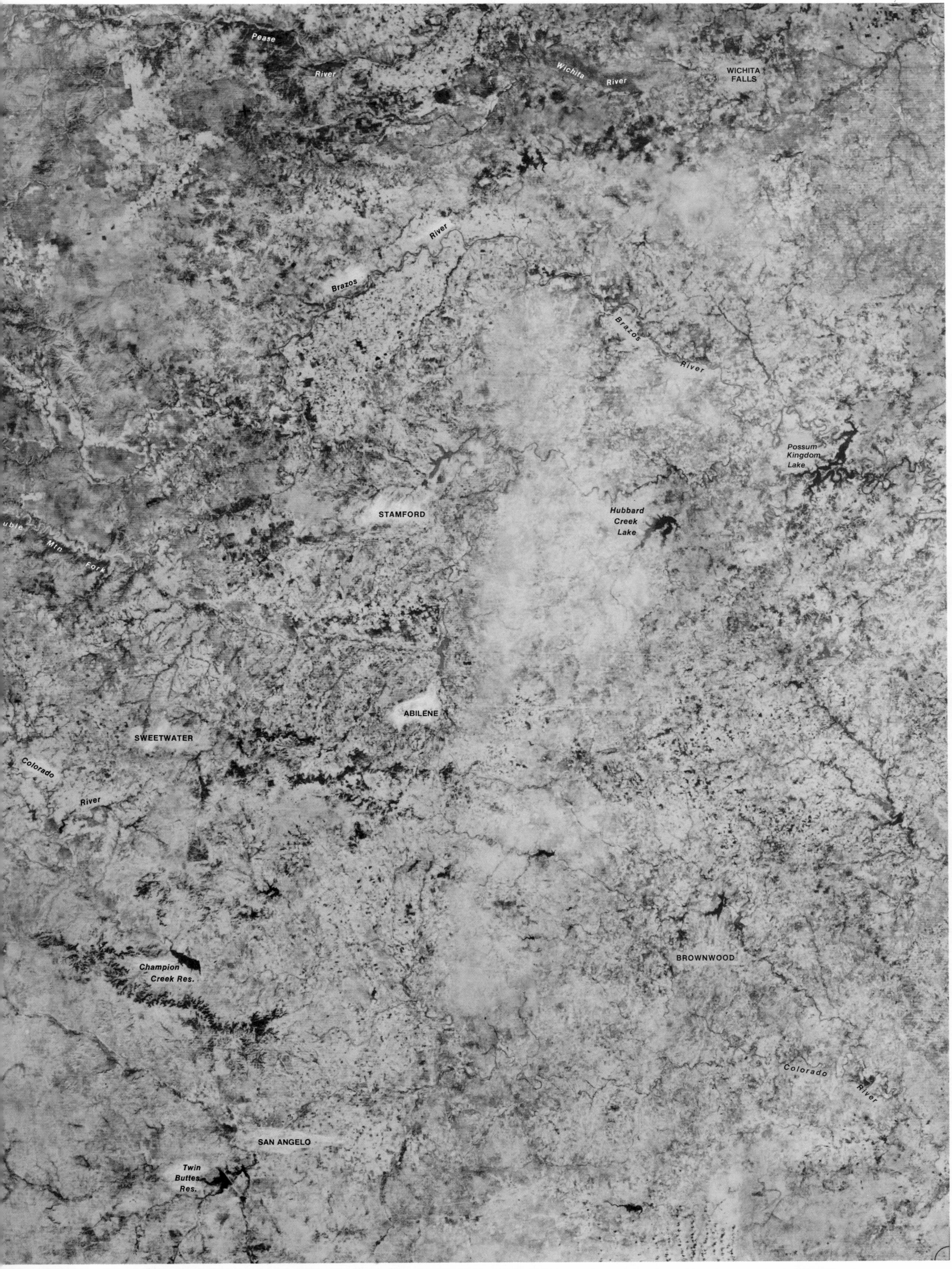

Pease

River

Wichita River

WICHITA FALLS

Brazos River

Brazos River

Possum Kingdom Lake

uble Mtn Fork

STAMFORD

Hubbard Creek Lake

ABILENE

SWEETWATER

Colorado River

BROWNWOOD

Champion Creek Res.

Colorado River

Pease

SAN ANGELO

Twin Buttes Res.

68

The **Edwards Plateau** extends from the **Pecos River** to the eastern edge of this photo-map. The southern boundary of the plateau is above the **Nueces Plains.** There are relatively few surface streams in this region. The plateau is composed largely of limestone, a material which dissolves fairly readily in ground water. Where water has dissolved away the limestone, underground caverns are formed and sub-surface rivers drain the area. Areas of such underground drainage springs and sinkholes are known as karst regions.

The **Edwards Plateau,** including the Texas Hill Country, is ranchland noted for sheep-ranching rather than cattle. Very little cropland can be seen in this photo-map. Native range grass dominates the relatively arid landscape, although traces of forests are visible in the northeastern portion of this photo-map around **Kerryville** and **Fredericksburg.** Rainfall approaches 25 inches annually to produce these woodlands.

Amistad Reservoir, northwest of **Del Rio,** was created by the construction of a 6½ mile long dam at the confluence of the **Rio Grande** and **Devils River.** The area surrounding the recently created lake is a National Recreation Project sponsored by both the U.S. and Mexican governments.

Besides being one of the primary sheep-ranching areas in the nation, the Texas Hill Country has a concentrated population of Angora goats. The goats can subsist on pastures rejected even by sheep. More than 95% of the U.S. mohair production is from these Angora goats. **Sonora** is located within this goat and sheep raising area and the city has become a major wool and mohair marketing center.

Big Bend National Park occupies the region within the U-shaped curve of the **Rio Grande** in the southwest corner of this photo-map. The **Chisos Mountains** lie within the park. In Spanish, chisos means phantoms, and the mountains were given this name because of their mirage-like appearance at certain times of the day. An inland sea covered this region millions of years ago. Shells and fossils remain as evidence of this period.

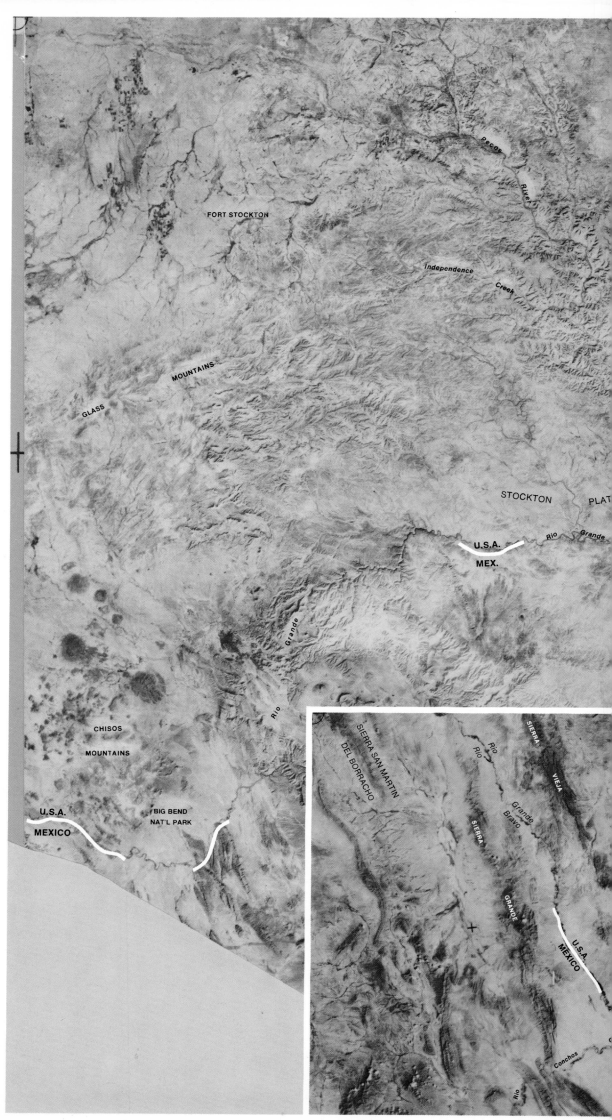

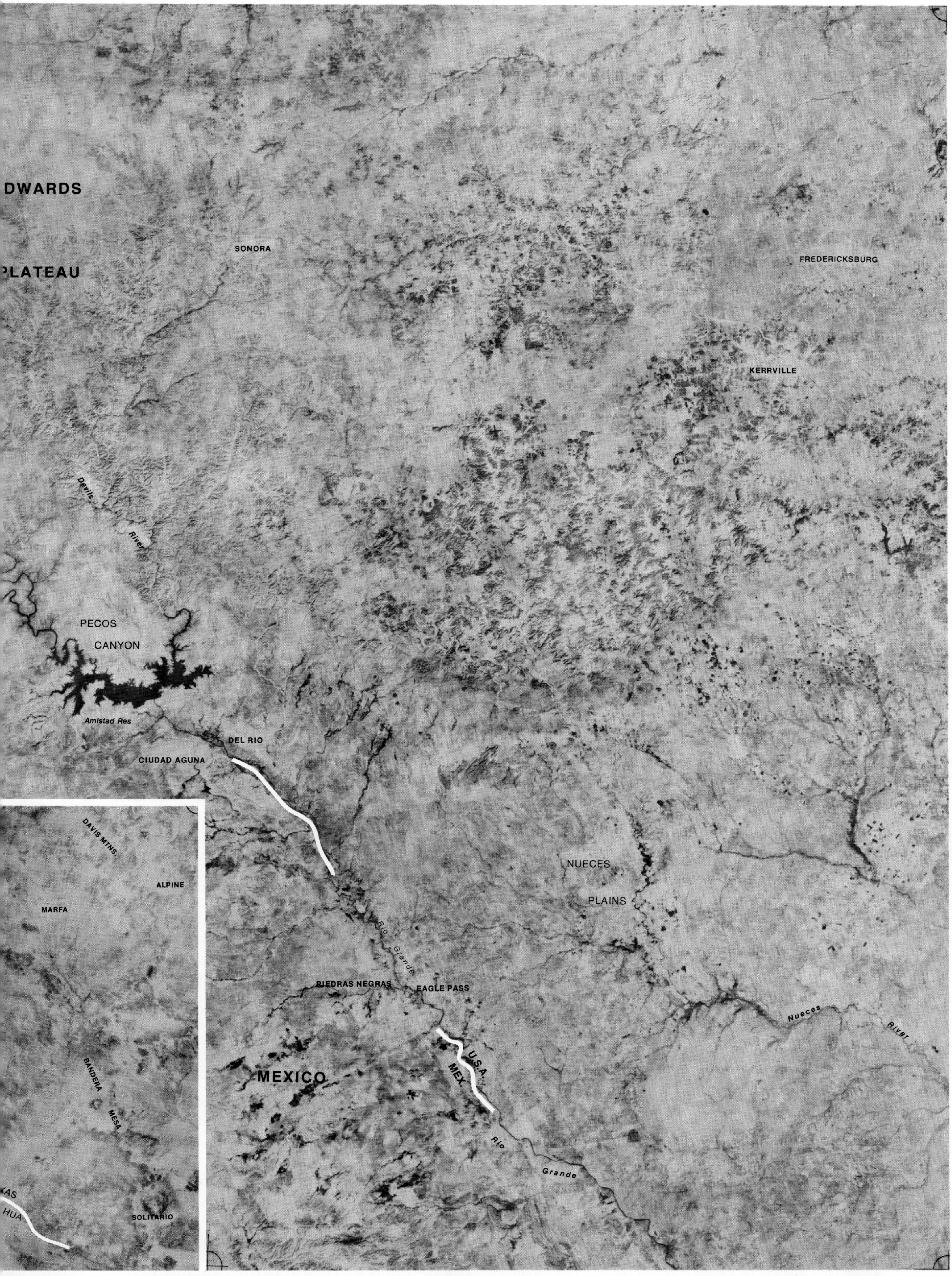

DWARDS

PLATEAU

SONORA

FREDERICKSBURG

KERRVILLE

Devils

River

PECOS
CANYON

Amistad Res

DEL RIO

CIUDAD AGUNA

NUECES

PLAINS

DAVIS MTNS

ALPINE

MARFA

Rio

Grande

Nueces

River

PIEDRAS NEGRAS

EAGLE PASS

BANDERA

MESA

U.S.A.

MEX.

MEXICO

Rio

Grande

XAS

HUA

SOLITARIO

Rainy Lake

INTERNATIONAL FALLS

Rainy River

ONT

MINN

CANADA

U.S.A.

SUPERIOR NATIONAL FO

Nett Lake

Pelican Lake

HILLS

Vermillion Lake

MISQUAH

SUPERIOR NAT'L FOREST

RANGE

SILVER BAY

MESABI

CHIPPEWA NAT'L FOREST

HIBBING

Lake Winnibigoshish

Island Lake Res.

TWO HARBORS

GRAND RAPIDS

CHIPPEWA NAT'L FOREST

Leech Lake

St. Louis

River

DULUTH

Big Sandy Lake

SUPERIOR

River

Mississippi

WISCONSIN

MINNESOTA

Rice Lake N.W.R.

Pelican Lake

Gull Lake

Mille Lacs Lake

BRAINERD

River

Croix

The area represented on this photo-map has been totally covered by the thick glaciers of the Ice Ages. The topography exhibits the results of the scraping and scouring action of ice sheets. The numerous lakes, swamps and bogs of glacial and ice-melting origin, lend a spongelike appearance to the region when viewed from space.

Geologists refer to the region on this photo-map as the Superior Upland. This area is a portion of the much larger system of rocks known as the Canadian Shield. The rocks found here are among some of the oldest exposed rocks in the world and they extend throughout much of Canada, Labrador and Greenland.

The **Mesabi Range** and the **Misquah Hills** west of **Lake Superior,** and the **Gogebic Range** east of the lake are the areas of greatest relief represented in this photo-map. Low rolling hills and plains dominate the rest of the landscape. Water from the northern Minnesota highlands flows in three directions to reach the ends of the continent: north to Hudsons Bay via the **Rainy River** and its tributaries; south through the **Mississippi River** System to the Gulf of Mexico; and east to the Atlantic Ocean by way of the **St. Louis River,** the Great Lakes, and the St. Lawrence River.

Several belts of iron ore have been found to parallel both the north and south coasts of **Lake Superior.** The **Mesabi Range** in Minnesota and the **Gogebic Range** in upper Michigan have been the outstanding sources of American iron ore. Some of the open pit mines in both areas are visible on this photo-map.

The **Keweenaw Peninsula** of Michigan has been a major U.S. source of copper since 1844. The copper and iron ores extracted from the region on this photo-map provided economic justification for the opening in 1855 of the Sault Ste. Marie or Soo Canal (see photo-map pp. 84-85). This extended shipping from **Lake Superior** to the industrial regions of the upper Midwest.

The small stream leaving the southeast corner of **Lake Winnibigoshish** is the **Mississippi River.**

Mille Lacs
Lake

Mississippi

River

ST. CLOUD

Mississippi

River

RICE LAK

River

St. Croix

Green
Lake

MINNEAPOLIS   ST. PAUL

Lake
Minnetonka

WILLMAR

Lake
Waconia

RED WING

Mississippi

River

Red

Chippe

Minnesota

REDWOOD
FALLS

ROCHESTER

Swan
Lake

NEW ULM

OWATONNA

MANKATO

River

Cottonwood

ST. JAMES

AUSTIN

ALBERT
LEA

Cedar

Wapsipinicon

Spirit
Lake

River

West
Okoboji
Lake

MASON
CITY

Clear
Lake

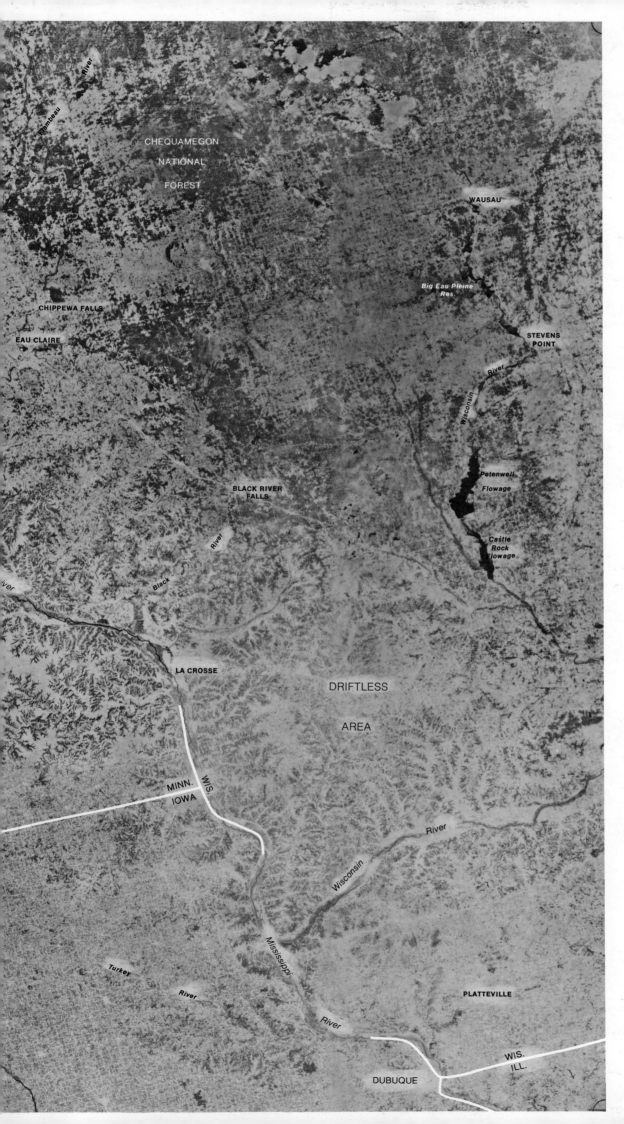

RAMBEAU River

CHEQUAMEGON

NATIONAL

FOREST

WAUSAU

Big Eau Pleine Res.

CHIPPEWA FALLS

EAU CLAIRE

STEVENS POINT

Wisconsin River

BLACK RIVER FALLS

River

Petenwell Flowage

Black

Castle Rock Flowage

River

LA CROSSE

DRIFTLESS

AREA

MINN.

WIS.

IOWA

River

Wisconsin

Mississippi

Turkey

River

PLATTEVILLE

River

WIS.

ILL.

DUBUQUE

The delicate white patterns just north of **Redwood Falls,** Minnesota (in the western portion of this photo-map) appear to be clouds. The Landsat imagery, from which this mosaic of the United States was produced, was obtained repeatedly over each area every 18 days.

Virtually all of the United States north of the Ohio and Missouri Rivers was covered by thick ice sheets during the Ice Ages. An exception is the southwestern corner of Wisconsin and the adjacent parts of Illinois, Minnesota and Iowa. This area was bypassed, but completely surrounded by the thick glacial ice. Known as the Driftless Area, the topography in this region is sculpted more by the action of wind and the waters of the **Mississippi** and **Wisconsin Rivers,** than by the smoothing action of ice sheets.

Tourists are attracted to the scenic topography of the **Driftless Area** and adjacent regions such as the Wisconsin Dells (on the **Wisconsin River,** south of the **Castle Rock Flowage.**)

The more irregular landscape of the **Driftless Area** is reflected in this photo-map by a breakdown of the normally square patterns of roads and agricultural fields characteristic of most of the midwestern United States.

Minneapolis and **St. Paul** lie at the head of navigation on the **Mississippi River** and are important grain milling and industrial cities. **Minneapolis** was first settled as a sawmill town where north woods lumbermen could float their logs directly to the numerous mills along the river's edge.

When excessive cutting depleted the northern forests, the lumbermills were replaced by flour mills. An early settlement which became **St. Paul** was established around an Army fort and, until 1841, had the unusual name of Pig's Eye.

Lake Minnetonka, southwest of **Minneapolis,** is a popular summer resort for this area. The lake's outlet is Minnehaha or Laughing Water Creek which trickles north from the lake through **Minneapolis.** Minnehaha Falls, immortalized by Longfellow's poem Hiawatha, occur just before the small creek flows into the **Mississippi River.**

Des Moines River

Iowa River

Little Sioux River

Storm Lake

FT. DODGE

MARSHALLTOWN

BOONE

AMES

Racoon

ARION

Des Moines River

DES MOINES

Red R Res

HARLAN

Boyer River

ATLANTIC

CRESTON

COUNCIL BLUFFS

OMAHA

GLENWOOD

Platte River

West Nishnabotna River

SHENANDOAH

Thompson River

NEBR

IOWA

MO.

MARYVILLE

Missouri River

FALLS CITY

The land in this photo-map was levelled and the soils enriched by the large sheet of glacial ice which moved from the north thousands of years ago to cover the region. Today, the area is overlaid with a thick layer of windblown silt, known as loess, which was deposited during and shortly after glacial times. Strong winds which blew along the margins of the ice sheets picked up fine particles from the wide floodways formed by the melting glaciers and transported these silty particles to adjacent areas, depositing them thickly along streams. This loess added to the richness of the soils of much of Iowa, Illinois, and other Midwestern states.

The western Corn Belt extends throughout this photo-map. Iowa, Nebraska and Illinois lead the nation in corn production. Since World War II, soybeans have also been raised extensively in this area.

Iowa is dominated by a gently undulating landscape which flattens out to the east. The intensity and regularity of the croplands surrounding **Cedar Rapids** and **Iowa City** is apparent on this photo-map. Ninety-four percent of the state of Iowa is devoted to agriculture.

Appropriately located in the heart of the Corn Belt on the border of Illinois and Iowa is a group of cities forming the farm implement capital of the world. Major cities in this agglomeration of industrial centers at the confluence of the Rock and **Mississippi Rivers** are **Rock Island** and **Moline,** Illinois and **Davenport,** Iowa.

Omaha, located at the confluence of the **Missouri** and **Platte Rivers,** is well-situated for its important meat-packing industry. It stands between the rangelands to the west, and the markets to the east, and is surrounded by feed grain producers.

Council Bluffs, Iowa, across the **Missouri River** from **Omaha,** takes its name from the Indian meetings and ceremonies held on the bluffs above the river.

Hannibal, Missouri, on the banks of the **Mississippi** north of St. Louis, is the boyhood home of Mark Twain. Twain used the **Hanibal** region as the setting for many of the adventures of Tom Sawyer and Huckleberry Finn.

NEBRASKA
KANSAS

ST. JOSEPH

MO.
KANS

Perry
Res

KANSAS CITY

INDEPENDENCE

Kansas   River

LAWRENCE   TOPEKA

South   Grand

EMPORIA

Osage

John Redmond
Res

FLINT

Fall River
Res.

Neosho

HILLS

River

Verdigris

Walnut

River

INDEPENDENCE

JOPLIN

MISSOURI

KANSAS
OKLAHOMA

COFFEYVILLE

Lake
O'Cherokees

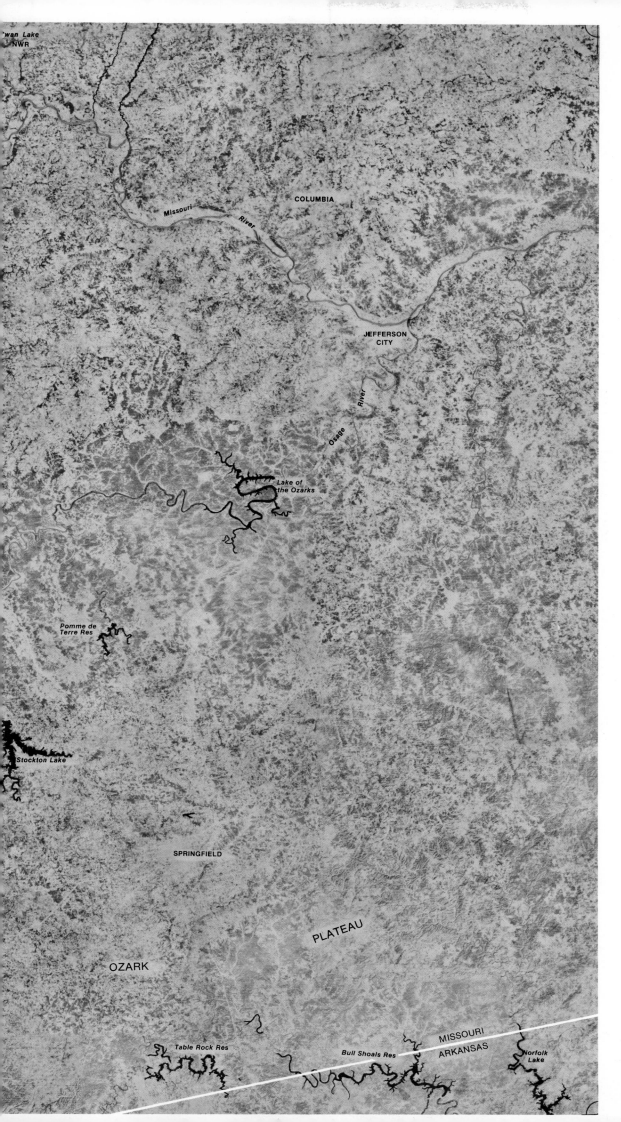

Several of the nineteenth-century overland trails originated from **St. Joseph,** Missouri. Pioneers moving westward along the Oregon Trail could no longer rely on established forms of water or overland transport and struck out across the prairies in wagon trains. In 1860, the first Pony Express rider began his trip from St. Joe to Sacramento, California.

Kansas City and its surrounding communities are apparent on the photo-map as a sprawling, light shaded area. This is the typical signature of an urban area. The U.S. Weather Bureau has its severe storms center located in **Kansas City.** Tornadoes are more frequent in this region and in the surrounding states than anywhere else in the nation. The climate here is extreme in other ways. Summers are hot and humid and winters are cold.

Infamous old west characters were prominent in this region a century ago. Quantril raided **Lawrence,** devastating it and killing every man he saw. Jesse James was an infamous resident of the **St. Joseph,** Missouri area, and the Dalton gang was nearly wiped out when they robbed the bank of Coffeyville, Kansas.

Unlike the plains to the west, the region in this photo-map has adequate rainfall for most forms of agriculture, averaging around 35-40 inches of precipitation annually. However, variations in the landforms and geology greatly influence agricultural activity, which ranges from rather limited general farming in the northeastern margin of the **Ozark Plateau** (lower right), to the grazing land of the **Flint Hills** along the western margin of this photo-map. In between, lies better agricultural land. Some wheat is grown, but generally the crops are more representative of the Corn Belt to the east. Corn, soybeans, grain sorghums, and alfalfa are major crops.

The **Flint Hills,** a pleasant relief from the flatter topography of Kansas to the west, tend to have thin, rocky soils. Because of this, these hills are the only sizeable portion of the North American plains and prairies which have never been plowed. Cattle graze on the native grasses of the rolling hills.

BARTLESVILLE

PONCA CITY

Oologa Res

Arkansas

River

TULSA

Ft. Gibson
Res.

Keystone Res.

River

Cimarron

MUSKOGEE

Tenkiller
Ferry Res.

Deep *Fork* *River*

OKMULGEE

Short Mtn Res.

Eufala
Res.

OKLAHOMA
CITY

SHAWNEE

North *River*

Canadian

McALESTER

Canadian *River*

OUACHITA

Washita *River*

Arbuckle
Res.

ARDMORE

Lake
Murray

Lake
Texoma

Red *River*

MO.
AR.

PARIS

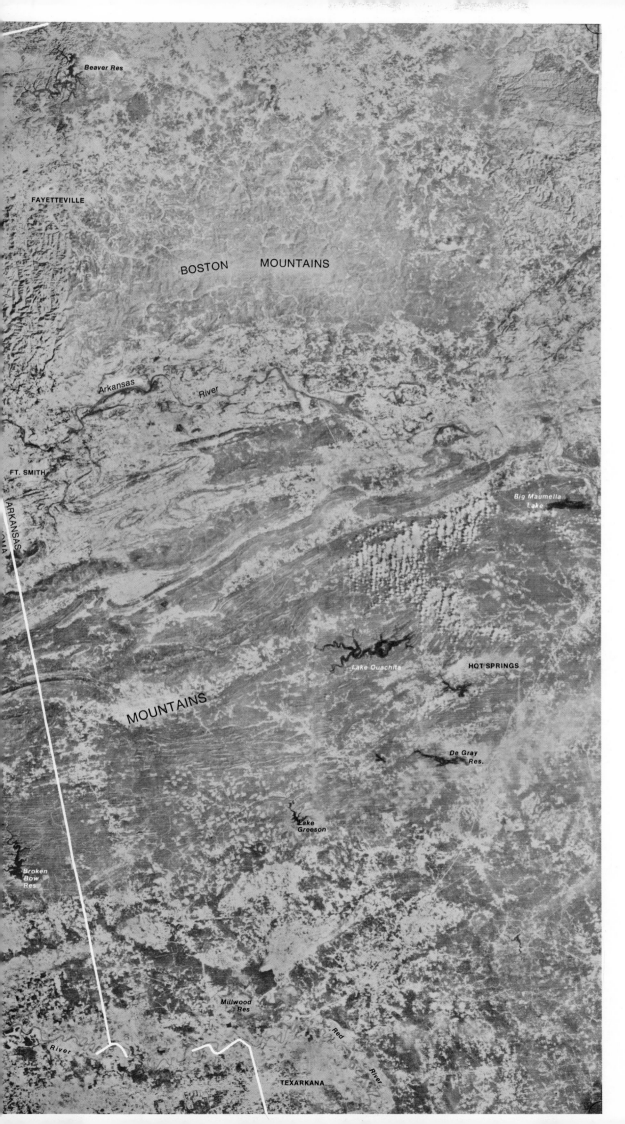

One can see the results of dramatic contortions which portions of the earth's surface have undergone in the geologic past. Even from Landsat, over 500 miles in space, the folding and faulting of the **Ouachita Mountains** is evident. These structures are not excessively high (elevations range from 300 to 2,700 feet in the mountains), but the tilted and folded beds of shale, slate, sandstone, and other rocks have been exposed and eroded into a series of parallel, curving ridges.

The **Ouachita Mountains,** like the Uintas in Utah, have an east-west orientation which is extremely rare among mountain ranges in the United States. The **Ouachita** and the **Boston Mountains** to the north are covered with oak, hickory, and pine forests, some of which are commercially logged. The remainder of the area is a mixture of cropland, pasture, and woodland. The most heavily cropped portion is in the south.

The type of agriculture carried on in the western portion of this photo-map is called general farming, for lack of a more definitive term. Most farms are small and are often much more like the self-sufficient family farms of the past than the trend toward specialization and commercialism characteristic of most U.S. farms today. Corn is the most common raw crop, but a diverse mixture of crops in small patches is found here. Livestock is also important. The patchwork of small and irregularly shaped fields is not apparent from the altitudes at which the photo-images in this photo-map were obtained. Instead, the darker tones of the mixed woodlands dominate.

This region lies between the corn-soybean belt to the northeast, the cotton belt to the south, the wheat belt to the northwest, and the arid grazing lands to the west. Examples of each are represented here.

Oil production is significant in the western portions of this photo-map. **Tulsa,** of course, owes its major significance to being a petroleum center. The rich East Texas Oilfield, the largest known pool in the nation, extends northward in this region, at least to the **Canadian River.**

OKLA.

TEXAS

Red River

Red

Sulphur

Lavon
Res

Garza-Little
Elm Res

Lake
Tawakoni

Grapevine
Res

Sabin

DALLAS

FT. WORTH

Trinity

Brazos

Benbrook
Lake

River

Cedar
Creek
Res

River

CORSICANA

Lake
Whitney

Trinity

MEXIA

River

Leon

River

Navasota

River

WACO

Brazos

River

Belton
Lake

KILLEEN

Stillhouse
Hollow Res.

BRYAN

This photo-map shows two distinct regions. The darker-appearing eastern half is the Piney Woods and the western half is the Texas Black Prairie agricultural land. The Piney Woods region, where the dominant trees are pine, hickory and post oak, contains the **Sam Houston National Forest.** In addition to cattle, the agriculture of the Black Prairie includes such diverse crops as watermelon and pecans. The dominate crop, however, is cotton.

The **Red River** crosses the northeast corner of this photo-map. Its flood plain is defined by a broad, light band.

The economics of the burgeoning twin cities of **Dallas** and **Fort Worth** illustrate the fact that this area straddles the rangelands to the west and the intensive agriculture and commerce to the east and north. **Fort Worth** has traditionally had an emphasis on cattle, railroads, and industry while **Dallas** is concerned more with oil, finance, and commerce.

Between **Dallas,** Texas and **Shreveport,** Louisiana lies the East Texas Oilfield. It was considered an unlikely area for oil exploration until a wildcatter struck oil there in 1930. Although this relatively small area has been peppered with 27,000 oil wells, it still remains the most productive oil field in the nation. The boomtown of Kilgore, just southwest of **Longview,** Texas is dominated by a forest of oil derricks.

There was a slight cloud problem when the photo-image showing the Dallas-Fort Worth area used in this photo-map was taken. The photo-image was included because it gives an excellent portrayal of the extent of the Dallas-Fort Worth urban and suburban land usage. The light area is the signature, or distinctive reflectance pattern, of an urbanized area.

The Dallas-Fort Worth International Airport is the white bug-shaped area (promoters say it's the shape of a dollar sign) halfway between the two cities and slightly to the north. It is the largest airport in the world and was built in the hope of improving this land-locked area's link with other parts of the nation and the world.

Lake Lyndon
B Johnson

Lake Travis

AUSTIN

Canyon Res

Colorado   River

Somerville Res.

SAN ANTONIO

VICTORIA

Guadalupe

River

San   Antonio   River

Waterway

Frio

River

Intracoastal

Nueces   River

ARANSAS
PASS

CORPUS
CHRISTI

Corpus Christi
Bay

FREER

ALICE

Laguna   Madre

KINGSVILLE

Sediment plumes can be seen at the outflow of the embayments and estuaries, and into the Gulf of Mexico. Southwestward down the Gulf Coast more sediment outflows can be seen, indicating the activity of currents near the shore.

The black streaks on the water south of **Freeport** are typical of oil slicks. These are probably the result of the many petroleum-related activities in this section of the **Gulf of Mexico.**

The small light areas north of **Brownsville,** along the coast, are sand dunes. Sand dunes can also be seen on the barrier beaches that line most of the Texas Gulf Coast.

Keweenaw
Point

Lake   Superior

Keweenaw
Bay

BIG BAY

HURON   MOUNTAINS

Grand
Island

Laughing
Fish Pt.

Tahquamenon

River

MARQUETTE

SENEY
N.W.R.

Manistique
Lake

Lake
Michigamme

ISHPEMING

HIAWATHA

NAT'L

FOREST

Indian
Lake

MANISTIQUE

Michigamme
Res.

High
Island

Beaver
Island

GLADSTONE

Big Bay
De Noc

ESCANABA

Brule   River

South
Fox
Island

IRON MTN.

Cedar

KINGSFORD

MICH.

WIS.

River

Washington
Island

Menominee

NICOLET

River

North
Manitou
Island

NAT'L

South
Manitou
Island

FOREST

MENOMINEE

MARINETTE

JACKSONPORT

MOUNTAIN

Crystal
Lake

STURGEON
BAY

FRANKFORT

Lake   Michigan

Green

SHAWANO

GREEN
BAY

KEWAUNEE

MANISTEE

Lake Superior, Lake Huron and **Lake Michigan** are (in that order) the three largest lakes in North America, with depths of 1,333 feet, 750 feet, and 923 feet, respectively.

Most lakes in this region are due to glaciation, but it is difficult to explain depths such as that of **Lake Superior** in terms of glacial action. Current geologic thinking interprets this deep trench as a separation in the North American continental crust. As seen on the index map (pages 4 and 5), **Lake Superior** appears to form a semi-circle with the Georgian Bay, roughly concentric to and outside the semi-circle formed by **Lake Michigan** and **Lake Huron.**

Sault Ste. Marie, though the oldest town in Michigan, is better known for the navigational locks which allow ships and barges to avoid the rapids separating **Lake Superior** from **Lake Huron.** Over 100 million tons of freight pass through the locks annually.

The **Nicolet National Forest** marks the southern extent of the vast northern hardwood forest, and includes yellow birch, maple, beech, pine, and balsam fir. The boundary between the dark, solid shades of the forest and the lighter agricultural lands can clearly be seen on this photo-map west of **Green Bay.**

The eastern shore of **Lake Michigan** is noted for fruit production, especially peaches and cherries. The dominant winds blow from the west across the lake and therefore tend to moderate the climate along the Michigan shore.

Michigan, a land of peninsulas and lakes, is aptly named from the Indian "michi gami"—a great water.

For almost 2 years of photographing this area, there were no cloud-free pictures. Speculation credited the cloud problem to the fact that the 18-day cycle of Landsat coverage is a multiple of the 6-day weather cycle of current meterological theory.

Finally, cloud-free imagery was obtained, with the exception of the scattered, fluffy clouds to the north of **Houghton Lake.** A light snow fall can be seen around **Saginaw Bay** in the southeastern corner of this photo-map.

NEW LONDON

Fox River

APPLETON

MANITOWOC

LUDINGTON

Lake Winnebago

Lake Poygan

OSHKOSH

SHEBOYGAN

Little Sable Pt.

RIPON

FOND DU LAC

Green Lake

PORT WASHINGTON

Fox Lake

Beaver Dam Lake

PORTAGE

MENOMONEE FALLS

Lake Wisconsin

MILWAUKEE

Lake Michigan

Lake Mendota

MADISON

WAUKESHA

Lake Monona

RACINE

Lake Koshkonong

KENOSHA

JANESVILLE

LAKE GENEVA

Lake Geneva

WAUKEGAN

BELOIT

MONROE

WISCONSIN

ILLINOIS

EVANSTON

ROCKFORD

ELGIN

CHICAGO

FREEPORT

Rock River

GARY

ROCHELLE

AURORA

Des Plaines River

HAMMOND

DIXON

JOILET

IND.

ILL.

STERLING

Fox River

MENDOTA

Illinois River

Kankakee River

Rock River

KANKAKEE

Countless depressions in the surface, which are visible on this photo-map as lakes, are the result of continental glaciation. The direction of glacial movement can be seen in the northwest trending features just south of **Beaver Dam Lake.** The snow-fed lakes and many streams in this region supply **Milwaukee** with excellent brewing water.

The flat agricultural land in the southern half of the photo-map is one of the most productive parts of the corn and soybean regions of the United States. The Public Land Survey grid pattern is interrupted by rivers and scattered cities.

Madison, Wisconsin, the state capital and site of the University of Wisconsin, is located on an isthmus between **Lake Mendota** and **Lake Monona.**

The **Rock River** is the focus for small-to-medium-sized industrial cities in southern Wisconsin and northern Illinois. **Janesville** and **Beloit,** Wisconsin and **Rockford** and **Dixson,** Illinois mark the course of the river in its traverse across this photo-map.

Chicago lies at a critical point for inland water transportation in North America. The **Mississippi River System** is linked to the Great Lakes System by way of the **Illinois** and **Des Plaines Rivers** and canals through **Chicago.**

Chicago is the center of American transportation. Many transportation arteries, including highways, railways, and waterways can be seen on this photo-map heading toward and away from Chicago. A more detailed view of the **Chicago** area is provided in a full-color photo-map on the cover.

During the past several decades, rainfall records indicate an increased amount of precipitation in a portion of northwestern Indiana. Some scientists link this with the increased microscopic particulate matter thrown into the atmosphere by the steel mills and other sources along the southern shore of **Lake Michigan.** Moist air blowing from the lake apparently forms into droplets of water with these particles as nuclei and falls as rain a short time later downwind. The images used in this photo-map were taken on a clear day, but the phenomenon has been observed in other satellite photography, including the photo-map on the cover.

Rock River

KANKAKEE

LA SALLE

PRINCETON

STREATOR

Iroquois

KEWANEE

PONTIAC

River

Illinois

ILLINOIS

GALESBURG

Macinaw

River

PEORIA

BLOOMINGTON

RANTOUL

PEKIN

D

Spoon

CANTON

CHAMPAIGN

Sangamon River

River

LINCOLN

DECATUR

BEARDSTOWN

River

SPRINGFIELD

Lake
Shelbyville

MATTOON

Embarras River

JACKSONVILLE

Illinois

ILL
MO

Kaskaskia River

River

Mississippi

Little

Wabash

ALTON

Carlyle
Res.

River

River

ST. LOUIS

EAST ST. LOUIS

MT. VERNON

Missouri River

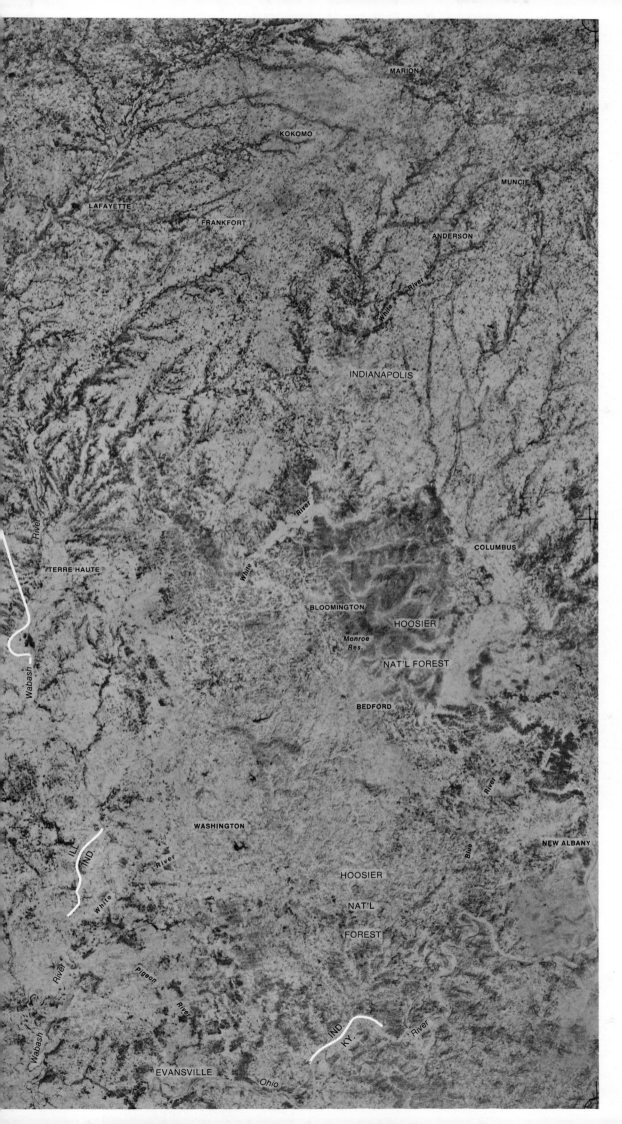

MARION

KOKOMO

MUNCIE

LAFAYETTE

FRANKFORT

ANDERSON

White River

INDIANAPOLIS

River

COLUMBUS

TERRE HAUTE

White

BLOOMINGTON

HOOSIER

Monroe
Res.

NAT'L FOREST

BEDFORD

River

Wabash

WASHINGTON

NEW ALBANY

ILL.
IND.

River

Blue

White

HOOSIER

NAT'L

River

Wabash

FOREST

Pigeon

River

IND.
KY.

River

EVANSVILLE

Ohio

The center of this photo-map—the light colored area between **Kankakee** and **Mattoon,** Illinois—is the "Grand Prairie." This is one of the best, sizeable, natural agricultural areas in the world; certainly conditions are ideal for the growing of corn. Summers are hot; rainfall is plentiful and usually dependably around forty inches a year; the land is extremely flat; and the soils are very fertile. The landscape is an almost continuous patchwork of corn or soybean fields. Strangely enough, this region was settled and cultivated only after the development of lesser agricultural lands around it. Early settlers, believing good farmland should grow trees, were leary of these grasslands, though the grasses grew six feet or more. There were real problems for settlement. Among the major problems was the marshy nature of the area. The great continental glaciers levelled this area and then retreated about eight to ten thousand years ago, leaving flat and potentially fertile swamp lands. Only after the laying of tile and other artificial drainage, did this area become the great agricultural area it is today.

To the south of the Grand Prairie the land is more dissected. Dark ribbons of woodland can be seen lining the streams. This surface dates from an earlier glacial period than the area to the north, and therefore shows more wear or erosion than the more recent glaciation. It lacks the benefits of fertility endowed by the most recent glaciation which stopped its southward advance roughly along a line south of **Indianapolis** to around **Mattoon,** Illinois to between **Decatur** and **Springfield** and then roughly northward. The differences in the appearance of the areas on either side of the line in Illinois are dramatic.

The **Ohio River,** crossing the southeastern corner of this photo-map, is one of the busiest freight carriers in the world; tonnage exceeds that of the Panama Canal. Ships, carrying mostly heavy freight, are assured passage by the nine-foot-deep channel and a series of over forty locks and dams. The concentration of industry along the **Ohio River** and its tributaries has made it one of the most polluted rivers in the world.

Interstate 10

JACINTO CITY

Interstate 10

Memorial Park

Buffalo Bayou

Sam Houston Park

HOUSTON

Turning Basin

Port of Houston

GALENA PARK

Ship Channel

Gulf Freeway

Univ. of Houston

Brays Bayou

Forest Park Cemetery

PASADENA

W. UNIVERSITY PLACE

Rice Univ.

Hermann Park

Texas Southern Univ

Milby Park

Plum Creek

Brays Bayou

Old Spanish Trail

Glenbrook Golf Course

Interstate 610

Astrodome

Sims Bayou

Astroworld

SOUTH HOUSTON

WILLIAM P. HOBBY AIRPORT

Sims Bayou

Telephone Road

Gulf Freeway

Clear Creek

Creek

Clear

Houston

Houston is the product of petroleum. Its size and importance have paralleled the growth of oil as an important resource. One-tenth of the nation's crude oil is produced within 50 miles of Houston. The downtown area in the upper left center of this photo-map is marked by the shadows of skyscrapers, representing primarily the corporate head-quarters of oil companies or oil-related industries.

Houston is located not far from the Gulf of Mexico on a very flat, often wet coastal plain. Winters are mild and summers are hot and humid in this part of the nation.

The widening of **Buffalo Bayou**, a short ways downstream from the city center, indicates the head of the **Houston Ship Canal**, a waterway deepened and widened by dredging to accomodate large ocean-going

vessels. Today Houston ranks as the nation's third port in terms o tonnage, dominated by the transportation of oil and petro-chemica products. Storage tanks for these products can be seen lining the bank of the canal.

In terms of population growth, **Houston** is second only to Los Angele among the large cities of America, having tripled in population sinc 1940.

The round object in the left of the photo-map is the **Houston Astrodome.** North of the **Astrodome** is **Rice University** marked clearly b its football stadium and surrounding parking lot.

The Manned Spacecraft Center of the National Aeronautics and Spac Administration is just east of the area of this photo-map at Clear Lake.

New Orleans

New Orleans is in bayou country. The **Mississippi River** snakes across the picture on its way to the Gulf of Mexico downstream to the east. The banks of the river are high ground or levees, but away from the river are dark-appearing areas of backswamp seen to the left of the photo-map.

The long lot pattern of settlement along the **Mississippi River** is typical of areas colonized by the French. Each settler had a high and relatively dry location on the levee with good access to the waterfront. Homes and other structures were built on the levee with each settler's remaining holdings parcelled out in long strips extending back away from the stream.

New Orleans, the Crescent City, has spread far beyond its original site in the U-Shaped curve of the **Mississippi River** seen toward the lower right corner of the photo-map.

The French cultural heritage is not restricted to the **Vieux Carre** (French Quarter) adjacent to downtown **New Orleans.** French Acadians, now called Cajuns in Louisiana, were driven from Nova Scotia in the 1750's by the British when they gained control of Canada. Many Cajuns eventually resettled in the bayous where vestiges of their culture remain, including an unusual dialect of French.

Drainage and levee maintenance are a constant problem in **New Orleans** because the river may at times be twenty feet above the level of the city.

New Orleans has been an important port since colonial times. Its position near the mouth of the Mississippi helps it retain the position of second ranking port in the nation, yielding only to New York.

WASHINGTON

River

Kaskaskia

Mississippi

Rend
Lake

ILL.

MO.

River

CARBONDALE

Meramec

River

FLAT
RIVER

PERRYVILLE

River

CLARK

NAT'L

FOREST

ST. FRANCOIS

MOUNTAINS

CAPE
GIRARDEAU

Ohio

Current

River

CAIRO

MO.

K.Y.

Black

MARK TWAIN

POPLAR BLUFF

NAT'L FOREST

River

River

MISSOURI

ARKANSAS

KENNETT

Obion

River

MO.
TENN.

River

MISSOURI

ARKANSAS

MO.

ARK.

St. Francis

BLYTHEVILLE

River

JONESBORO

Black

Mississippi

Hatchie

White

River

NEWPORT

MEMPHIS

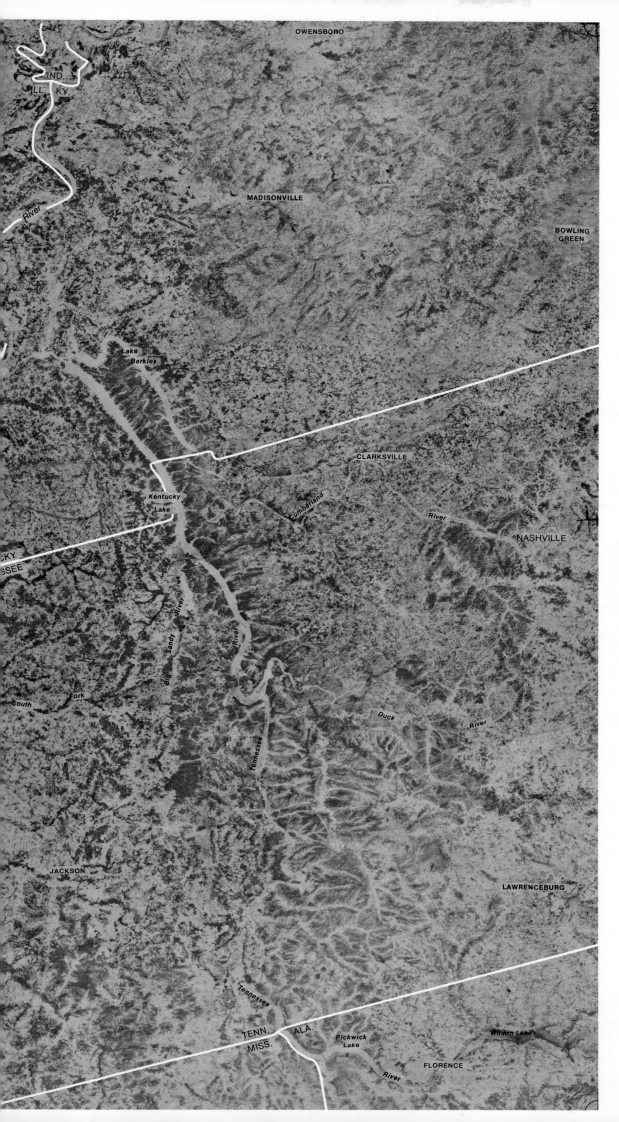

Carbondale, Illinois owes its name to the coal deposits common in southern Illinois. Indications of strip-mining activity can be seen in an east-west strip across the state, and are especially noticeable east of **Carbondale.**

The first capital of the state of Illinois was the town of **Kaskaskia,** at the juncture of the **Mississippi** and **Kaskaskia Rivers.** Years after the capital had been moved, the **Mississippi** changed its course, causing the former Illinois capital to be on the Missouri side of the river. However, it was allowed to remain a part of Illinois.

At the southern tip of Illinois, the valley of the **Mississippi River** changes character. To the north, the river is confined to a rather narrow floodplain and flows in a relatively straight course. At Thebes Gap, near **Cape Girardeau,** Missouri, the **Mississippi** bursts out onto a wide floodplain varying from 25 to 125 miles wide. The valley is often bounded by steep-sided walls up to 200 feet high. The river itself begins a much more meandering pattern along its southern course.

In 1933 the Tennessee Valley Authority was organized to control flooding on the **Tennessee River.** Today, virtually the entire length of the river and its tributaries (some 40,000 square miles) is a series of dams and reservoirs. The river is navigable from Knoxville (see photo-map pp. 102-103) to the **Ohio River.**

In the right portion of this photo-map, east of **Paducah,** Kentucky, are two of the lakes in the series created by the Tennessee Valley Authority. **Kentucky Lake** and **Lake Barkley.** Between the two lakes is a park and recreation area.

West of the **Mississippi River,** on this photo-map, is the Ozark Plateau. To the east, is the Jackson Plain, separating the Mississippi from the **Tennessee River.** The Appalachian highlands begin east of the Tennessee River.

The northern portion of the **Mississippi River** flood plain is shown on this photo-map. The rich alluvial soil plus an abundant supply of water make this region one of the most luxurient in the country.

MEMPHIS

Greers Ferry
Res.

FORREST
CITY

Arkabutla
Res

LITTLE ROCK

White

River

White

ARK.

MISS.

River

Arkansas

River

PINE BLUFF

River

Mississippi

CLEVELAND

GREENWOOD

MONTICELLO

WARREN

GREENVILLE

Ouachita

Yazoo

River

YAZOO CITY

River

EL DORADO

ARK.

LA.

Black

River

River

BASTROP

Yazoo

River

Big

Yazoo

VICKSBURG

MONROE

The wide floodplain of the **Mississippi River** dominates the western portion of this photo-map. The river has ambled across all parts of this floodplain at some time during its history, carving the wide valley. It sluggishly meanders along its way today, frequently bending its course as if reluctant to enter the **Gulf of Mexico** (photo-map pp. 96-97).

Changes in the **Mississippi River's** course are apparent. Former bends in the river have been cut off during flood stage to form ox-bow lakes. Many of these ox-bows can be seen on this photo-map. A large one is visible across the river from **Greenville,** Mississippi.

There is a diversity of croplands and woodlands in the wide **Mississippi River** floodplain. The land is relatively flat, but slight variations in elevation are significant for agriculture as well as natural vegetation. The backswamps are wet and the natural levees near the river are high and dry. The type of crop cultivated in this very important agricultural area is usually related to the differences in elevation and drainage.

The better drained, higher land along the **Mississippi River** is one of the major soybean growing areas in the nation.

The wetter areas in this region of relatively warm climate (usually dark areas on the photo-map) such as the land drained by the **White** and **Arkansas Rivers,** are naturally adaptable for growing rice.

Towering bluffs overlook the **Mississippi River** from the east or Mississippi side in this photo-map. **Vicksburg** is located atop a bluff directly above the river.

The **Yazoo River** originates just north of **Greenwood** (center of this photo-map) and parallels the course of the **Mississippi River** to the east, meandering along like its larger neighbor. The natural levee of the Mississippi is finally breeched by the **Yazoo River,** allowing it to merge with the Mississippi in the vicinity of **Vicksburg.**

The land east of the **Yazoo River** in this photo-map is characterized by low-rolling hills and short-leafed pine forests. Farther east in the vicinity of **Meridian,** is a prairie region that supports a thriving livestock and dairy industry.

Ouachita

River

Red

River

NATCHEZ

River

Homochitto

ALEXANDRIA

River

Red

MISS.

LA.

Mississippi

KISATCHIE

NAT'L.

FOREST

Atchafalaya

BATON ROUGE

River

River

LAFAYETTF

LATION

River

NEW IBERIA

LAKE CHARLES

Waterway

Intracoastal

Grand Lake

Vermilion Bay

Calcasieu
Lake

White   Lake

Marsh
Island.

Atchafalaya Bay

Point Au Fer Islan

GULF OF MEXICO

LAUREL

Chickasawhay River

Pascagoula River

HATTIESBURG

Pearl

River

BOGALUSA

River

BILOXI

Mississippi Sound

River

HAMMOND

Lake Maurepas

Lake Pontchartrain

Chandeleur

Islands

Lake Borgne

NEW ORLEANS

Lake Salvador

Mississippi

Breton Sound

Lafourche

River

DELTA NAT'L. WILDLIFE REFUGE

Barataria Bay

The Mississippi Delta

Terrebonne Bay

B

The dark areas in the northwest portion of this photo-map surrounding the **Red River** are primarily shortleaf-pine forests. This is Louisiana's major lumber producing area and **Alexandria** is the commercial center.

The importance of the fertile alluvial soils of river floodplains is apparent in this photo-map. The cultivated bottomlands of the **Red River Valley** are much lighter-toned than the surrounding woodlands.

Along the rivers in the **Baton Rouge** area, one can see a land use pattern characteristic of areas settled by the French. French colonials desired river access. They built their settlements in elongated villages on the higher land of the natural levees along the river margins. Their fields were laid out in long narrow patterns radiating, like spokes in a wheel, away from the river.

New Orleans lies between the **Mississippi River** and **Lake Pontchartrain.** Running north from **New Orleans** can be seen the longest bridge in the world. It is a twenty-four mile span across the lake.

Though well inland from the mouth of the **Mississippi River** and not a good natural harbor, **New Orleans** remains an important port because of the enormous amount of river traffic which is generated by the vast region served by the **Mississippi** and its tributaries.

The **Mississippi River's** outlet into the **Gulf of Mexico** can be seen in the lower right. The river carries a heavy load of silt eroded from the rich agricultural lands of the United States interior. Silt has piled up in the waters of the Gulf for thousands of years, building new land outward into the water to form a large, irregularly-shaped birdfoot delta.

The outlet of the **Mississippi River** has not always been at its present location. Former outlets were in the vicinity of **Atchafalaya Bay** and south of **Lake Borgne.** It appears that in a very few years the major course of the lower Mississippi may divert to the **Atchafalaya River,** a preferred route for running water because it is both shorter and steeper than the present course of the river.

SOUTHAMPTON

Lake *Huron*

Point
Clark

CANADA
U.S.A

CLOUDS

KITCHENE

Pt. aux Barques

PORT
AUSTIN

GODERICH

STRATFORD

BAD AXE

Fish Pt.

SANDUSKY

Kettle
Point

LONDON

ST. THOMAS

River

Thames

PORT
HURON

SARNIA

LAPEER

St. Clair River

FLINT

WALLACEBURG

Lake

PONTIAC

CHATHAM

Pointe
Aux Pins

Erie

DETROIT

Lake St. Clair

WINDSOR

DEARBORN

PAINESVILLE

ANN ARBOR

Pelee
Point

CLEVELAND

Pelee
Island

MONROE

Lake

Ontario

OSHAWA

CANADA
U.S.A.

TORONTO

ROCHESTER

Erie   Canal

LOCKPORT

BATAVIA

NIAGARA
FALLS

HAMILTON

Welland   Canal

CHEEKTOWAGA

Grand
River

RD

BUFFALO

SNOW

Genesee   River

ONT.
N.Y.

Peacock
Point

Long Point Bay

DUNKIRK

DA

Chautaugua
Lake

Allegheny
Res.

S.A.

JAMESTOWN

ERIE

NEW YORK
PENNSYLVANIA

River

ALLEGHENY

NAT'L FOR

Strip
Mine

River

Susquehanna

Allegheny

Bennet

LA

TITUSVILLE

Strip
Mines

West Branch

Pymatuning
Res

OIL CITY

DU BOIS

PENN
OHIO

CLARION

Strip
Mines

Mosquito
Creek
Res.

Strip Mining

YOUNGSTOWN

Water falling at the rate of 8,000 tons per second not only makes **Niagara Falls** a scenic attraction but also an excellent site for extensive hydro electric power production. The **Welland Canal** bypasses **Niagara Falls** and allows ships to pass between **Lake Ontario** and **Lake Erie** on their journeys.

Climbing 564 feet from **Albany** (see photo-map pp. 108-109) to **Buffalo** via 36 locks, the **Erie Canal** opened the west and made New York City the nation's primary port.

The grid patterns visible on this photo-map reflect the agricultural field patterns. The dark lines are rows of trees along the roads.

In the southeastern corner of this photo-map is an excellent example of scars on the land left by strip mining. The southern boundary at the **Allegheny National Forest** is well defined by white markings of strip mines against the dark shades of the wooded area. East of **Du Bois** and south of the **Bennet River** forest area, there is extensive strip mining visible on this photo-map. Similar scarring of the landscape occurs along the entire length of the Appalachian Mountains.

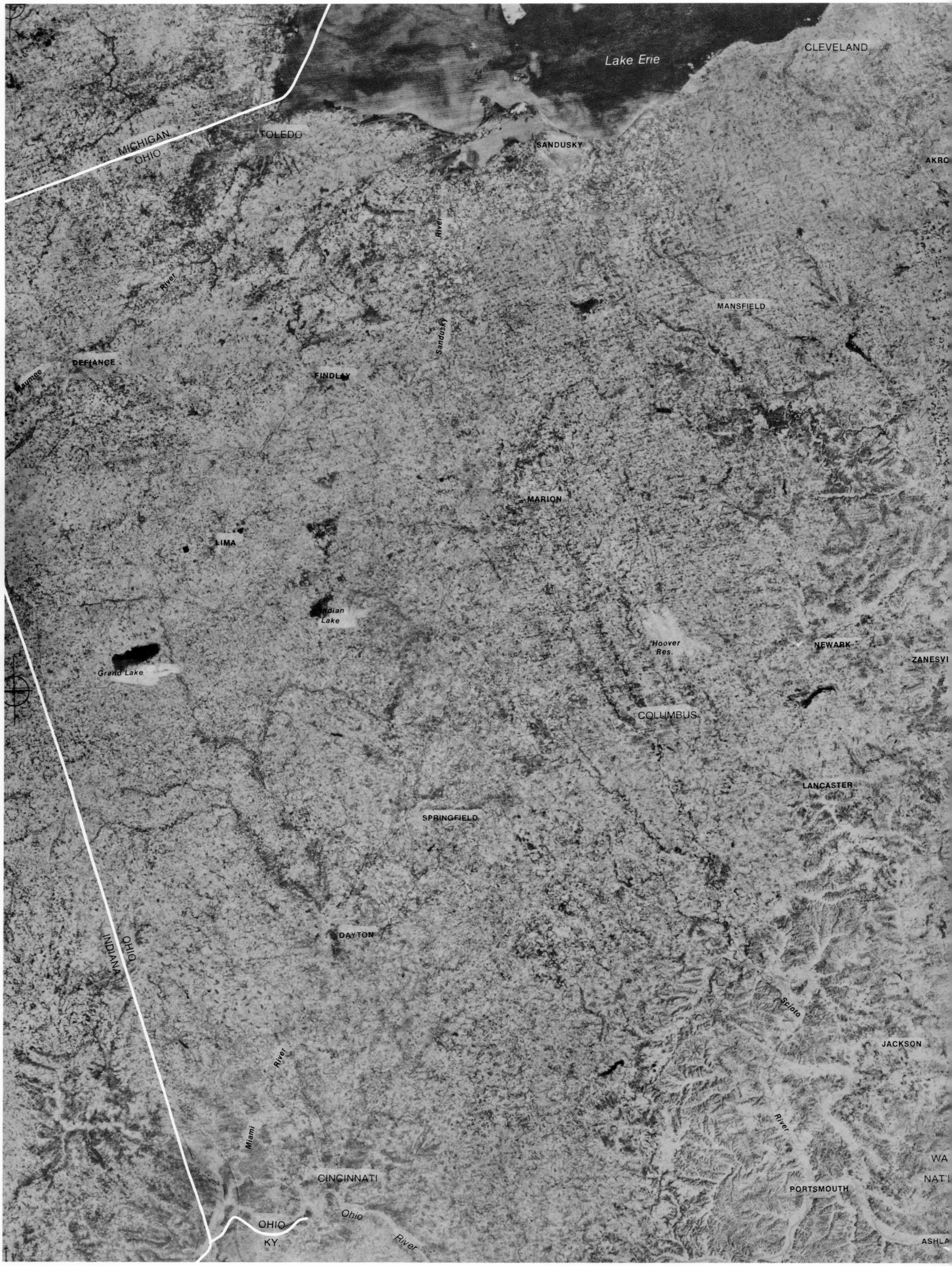

CLEVELAND

Lake Erie

MICHIGAN
OHIO

TOLEDO

SANDUSKY

AKRO

MANSFIELD

River

River

Sandusky

DEFIANCE

FINDLAY

Maumee

MARION

LIMA

Indian
Lake

NEWARK

Hoover
Res.

ZANESVI

Grand Lake

COLUMBUS

LANCASTER

SPRINGFIELD

DAYTON

Scioto

OHIO
INDIANA

JACKSON

River

Miami

River

WA
NAT'L

CINCINNATI

PORTSMOUTH

OHIO
KY.

Ohio

ASHLA

River

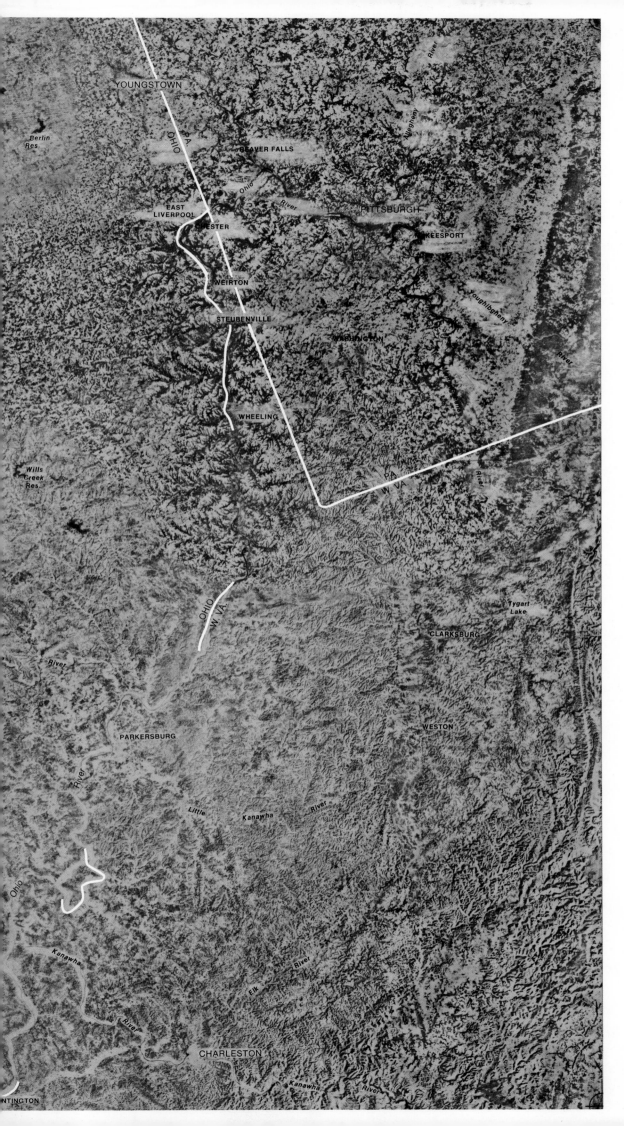

The south shore of **Lake Erie** reflects the action of glaciers thousands of years ago. The surface was smoothed over producing an almost flat, very gentle topography. Much of northwest Ohio around **Toledo** is an old glacial lake bed. The silt is ideal for the large number of tomatoes grown in the area. Breezes off **Lake Erie** have made the shoreline east of **Cleveland** a prominent grape growing area.

The intense industrialization along the Great Lakes has caused severe pollution problems. The Cuyahoga River near **Cleveland** will not support life due to the influx of industrial chemicals and by-products.

Coal from the Appalachians is shipped by rail to **Toledo** and transferred to ships on the Great Lakes making the city one of the world's leading soft coal ports.

Glaciers deposited tremendous amounts of material as they moved across Ohio. Hills were planed and the land leveled to produce today's gently rolling terrain.

The gently rolling terrain of Ohio was rapidly settled in the 1780's. The rectangular field demarcation system known as Township and Range was first introduced on a large scale in Ohio and continued as people moved west. The grid system of land ownership has resulted in the checkerboard appearance of farmland throughout the interior of the United States.

Built on a bluff above the river, **Cincinnati** is the largest city in the Ohio Valley. An important farm market and transportation center, the city earned the name Porkopolis for its meat-packing industry.

The **Monongahela River** is an important link in the steel industry. Coal from the Cumberlands is transported north to **Pittsburgh.** Before glaciers changed the river's course, the **Monongahela** and **Allegheny** flowed into the St. Lawrence River instead of forming the Ohio as they do today.

The concentration of steel industries in the **Cleveland, Youngstown, Pittsburgh** area has earned it the nickname, the Ruhr of America. Six of the largest steel producing cities in the country lie between **Cleveland** and **Pittsburgh.**

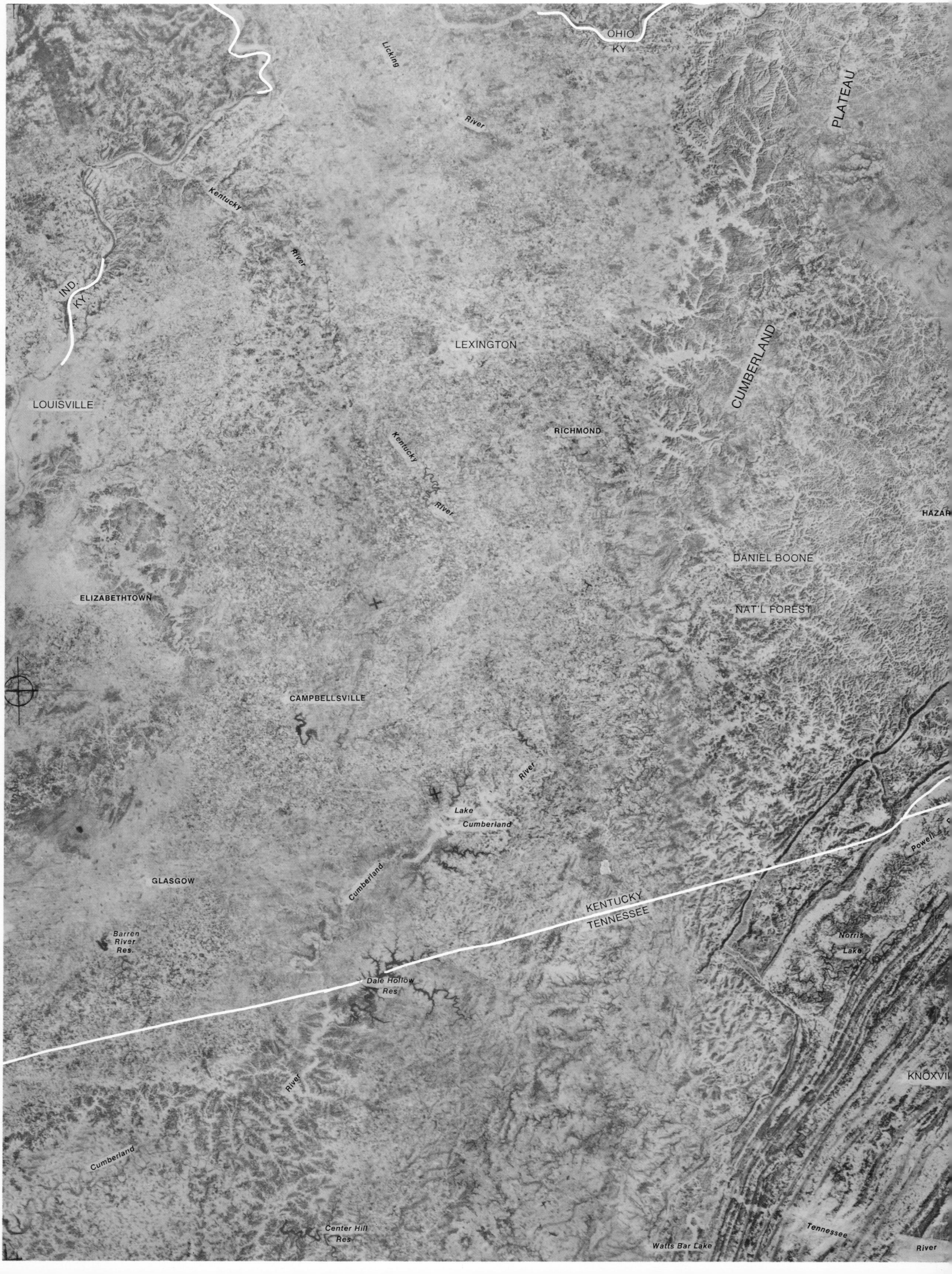

OHIO
KY

Licking

River

PLATEAU

Kentucky

River

CUMBERLAND

LEXINGTON

IND.
KY.

RICHMOND

LOUISVILLE

Kentucky

River

HAZAR

DANIEL BOONE

ELIZABETHTOWN

NAT'L FOREST

CAMPBELLSVILLE

River

Lake
Cumberland

Powell

GLASGOW

Cumberland

KENTUCKY

TENNESSEE

Barren
River
Res.

Norris
Lake

Dale Hollow
Res

River

KNOXVI

Cumberland

Center Hill
Res.

Tennessee

Watts Bar Lake

River

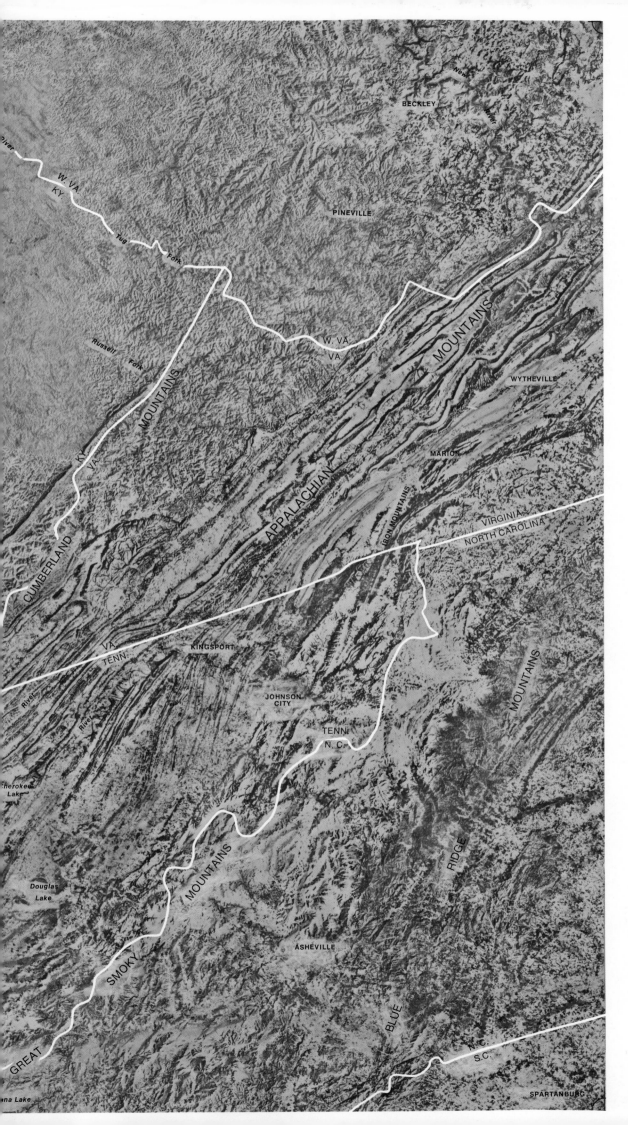

GREAT

SMOKY

MOUNTAINS

CUMBERLAND

MOUNTAINS

KY.
VA.

KY.
W. VA.

W. VA.
VA.

VA.
TENN.

TENN.
N. C.

N. C.
S. C.

APPALACHIAN

MOUNTAINS

BLUE

RIDGE

BECKLEY

PINEVILLE

WYTHEVILLE

MARION

IRON MOUNTAINS

VIRGINIA
NORTH CAROLINA

KINGSPORT

JOHNSON
CITY

ASHEVILLE

SPARTANBURG

Douglas
Lake

Cherokee
Lake

New
River

Tug
Fork

Russell
Fork

River

River

Millions of years ago the Appalachian area of the U.S. was pushed together by geologic forces and the land buckled. The result was the folded mountain complex of the **Appalachian Mountains.** Parallel ridges and valleys created formidable barriers as settlers attempted to push inland from the Atlantic Coast.

The Cumberland Plateau, lying to the west of the Appalachian Mountains is the site of extensive coal deposits, and has been excessively mined. **Strip mines** have left huge piles of refuse spewed over the hillsides. When it rains, water washes down the slopes eroding the soil and clogging the streams with sediment.

Lexington lies at the heart of the Kentucky Bluegrass Region, famous for its thoroughbred horse farms, bourbon whiskey distilleries, and burley tobacco production. The underlying limestone, hundreds of feet thick, is responsible for the fertile soils and rich green pastures that give the region its name.

Pioneers moving west bypassed West Virginia's mountains seeking easier passage north and south. Those who did settle here found a hard life of subsistence farming, lumbering, and coal mining. Mining has left much of the land unusable and many of the marginal farms are being abandoned in the heart of Appalachia.

At the southern end of the Appalachian chain, along the Tennessee-Carolina border, lie the **Great Smoky Mountains,** a rugged forest-covered range over 400 miles wide. As a conservation measure and to provide recreation, much of the area was incorporated into a national park.

The South has the mildest climate and receives the most rainfall of any large region in the U.S. In the **Smokies** over 80 inches fall annually.

Rugged and steep, the **Blue Ridge Mountains** are shrouded in dense forests. In the lowland farmers attempt to eke out a living on subsistence farms.

In the southern **Blue Ridge** and **Great Smoky Mountains** cultivated land can be found only in small valley pockets. Referred to locally as hollows, they can support only a few families on marginal farms.

Center
Hill
Res.

PLATEAU

River

Tennessee

Chickamauga
Lake

TULLAHOMA

CUMBERLAND

MOUNTAINS

TENN.
GA.

CHATTANOOGA

Blu
Rid
Lak

TENN.
ALA.

Elk

River

APPALACHIAN

HUNTSVILLE

Wheeler
Lake

Tennessee

Guntersville

Lake

River

Allato
Lake

LOOKOUT MTNS.

Weiss
Lake

Stone Quar

GLADSDEN

GEORGIA
ALABAMA

Lewis Smith
Lake

Chattahoochee

ANNISTON

River

LA C

Cooa

BIRMINGHAM

River

Warrior

TALLADEGA MTNS.

Black

ALEXANDER
CITY

Martin
Lake

The **Appalachian** highlands can be divided into four nearly parallel sections, all of which are represented on this photo-map: The Piedmont, the **Blue Ridge Mountains,** the Ridge and Valley section, and the **Cumberland Plateau. Spartanburg** and **Greenville,** South Carolina, and **Athens,** Georgia, are located in the area called the Piedmont (foot of the mountains). The Piedmont is bordered on the west by the **Blue Ridge Mountains. Chattanooga,** Tennessee lies in the Ridge and Valley section of the **Appalachians,** whose paralleling ridges (dark on the photo-map) and accompanying lowlands (lighter-toned) stand out in satellite photography. In contrast, the hills and valleys of the **Cumberland Plateau** to the west reveal no such orderly pattern.

The drainage patterns of several river systems are seen in the southeast portion of this photo-map. The geologic division of the United States, known as the Coastal Plain, begins here. Waterfalls along almost all of these rivers (the "fall line") mark the eastern boundary of the **Appalachian** Mountain System.

Macon, Georgia, at the head of the **Ocmulgee River,** is one of the series of cities located on this fall line which extends northeast as far as New Jersey. Waterfalls and rapids along the fall line are produced where the rivers leave the granite uplands of the mountains and begin their course through the more easily eroded clays and sands of coastal lowlands.

Greenville and **Spartanburg,** South Carolina were settled at the head of the navigable portion of the rivers that also provided water power for mills.

In the **Atlanta** and **Gainesville,** Georgia area are some of the purest marble deposits in the world. **Granite quarries** are also found in this region. Just north of **Atlanta** is the 800-foot-high Stone Mountain, the largest granite dome in the U.S.

The fertile **Tennessee River** Valley stretches across northern Alabama. **Guntersville Lake** is a holding reservoir for one of the dams constructed by the Tennessee Valley authority. Cotton and corn cultivation are the major economic factors of this area. To the south lie extensive coal and iron deposits.

TUSCALOOSA

BLACK

BELT

SELMA

Alabama

River

MONTGOMERY

GRADY

TROY

River

Conecuh

River

Tombigbee

River

Alabama

River

ALABAMA

FLORIDA

River

Conecuh

River

Yellow

River

Choctawhatehee Bay

FLA.

ALA.

MOBILE

Pensacola Bay

PENSACOLA

Mobile

PASCAGOULA

Perdido
Bay

Bay

GULF

OF

MEXICO

Bon Secour
Bay

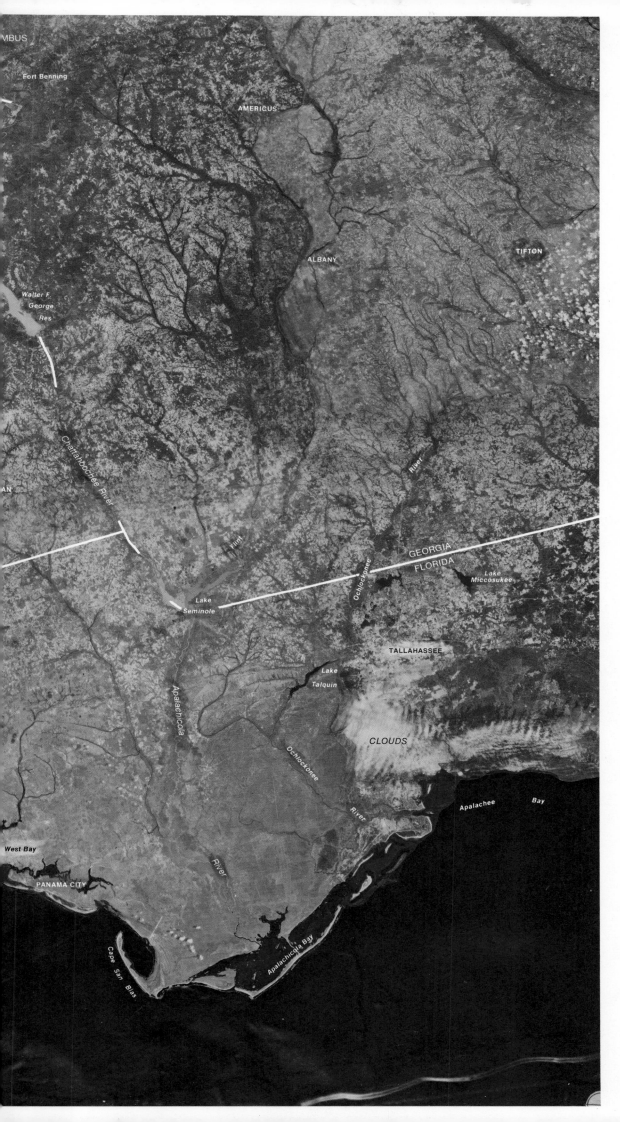

Columbus, Georgia, like Macon to the north (photo-map pp. 104-105), is located on the fall line, where easily eroded land meets more resistant materials, producing rapids in the rivers and streams. The coastal plain, with its well defined parallel and dendritic drainage systems, covers this entire photo-map.

In the upper left portion of this photo-map is the **Black Belt,** one of the most famous regions of the Old South. Rich soils, which produced an abundant cotton crop, made this a wealthy area, characterized by ante-bellum plantation mansions. The area was named for its black soils of weathered organic chalk, but it appears light on this photo-map because of extensive cultivation and the occurrence of Gum Trees that thrive in this soil. Marking the southern end of the **Appalachians,** the Black Belt stretches from **Montgomery,** Alabama to the western border of this photo-map, then curves north through Mississippi (photo-map pp. 94-95).

The uncultivated areas of Georgia in the upper right portion of this photo-map are predominantly pine forests. The Georgia pine yields a variety of products that are important sources of wealth to the state. Southern Georgia supplies three-fourths of the United States' and one-half of the world's naval stores (turpentine, pitch and resin). The state is the largest lumber producer in the U.S east of the Mississippi River.

Florida's Gulf coastline in this photo-map is characterized by lagoons, tidal marshes and offshore sand bars like **Cape San Blas.** Barrier beaches like the one extending from **Choctawatchee Bay** to **Pensacola Bay** indicate a shallow and sloping, sandy coast. Waves break off shore for great distances before reaching the mainland. The sand carried in front of these waves builds up to form a ridge that eventually protrudes above sea-level.

Mobile Bay, Pensacola Bay, and most of the other inlets which cut into the **Gulf of Mexico** Coast in this photo-map are drowned estuaries where the ocean has flooded the mouths of rivers.

VALLEYFIELD

St. Lawrence River

OTTAWA

CORNWALL

ONTARIO

NEW YORK

MASSENA

Lake
Champlain

SMITH FALLS

St. Lawrence River

OGDENSBURG

SARANAC LAKE

ADIRONDACK

MOUNTAINS

Thousand Islands

KINGSTON

WATERTOWN

Sacandaga
Res.

CANADA

U.S.A.

Mexico Bay

ROME

Mohawk

River

AMSTER

Lake

Ontario

Erie Canal

UTICA

OSWEGO

Oneida Lake

Otsego
Res.

COOPERSTOWN

SYRACUSE

AUBURN

ROCHESTER

Seneca Lake

Cayuga Lake

CA

The **White Mountains** of New Hampshire, a segment of the Appalachians, contain some of the highest mountain peaks in the Northeast. Formed by underground volcanic activity, the molten rock solidified into white and light colored granite, giving the mountains their name.

The **Vermont Valley** is apple country. Formed as a result of glaciers scouring the land, the valley's slopes are ideal for fruit while the valley itself is dotted with dairy farms.

Vermont ranks as one of the top states in marble and granite production. All the marble comes from the region west of the **Green Mountains,** but the largest quarries are located around **Rutland.** Granite quarries are predominant in the **Barre** area south of **Montpelier.** Slate for roofing material is mined along the Vermont-New York border.

Glaciers moving south between the **Adirondacks** and the **Green Mountains** gouged out the **Lake Champlain Valley,** a prominent dairy and recreation region in the Northeast.

By deepening channels and building locks like those just south of **Cornwall,** Ontario, the **St. Lawrence River** became navigable for ocean-going ships. Cities on **Lake Ontario** and the other Great Lakes are now ocean ports, particularly for grain and iron ore.

In the area where the **St. Lawrence River** drains from **Lake Ontario** is a group of picturesque, tree-covered islands known as the **Thousand Islands.**

Utica, Rome and **Syracuse,** New York were all settled in colonial times by pioneers pushing westward along the **Mohawk River Valley.** The route of the **Erie Canal** follows these cities. Upon its completion in 1825, growth and prosperity came to this area. **Syracuse** is noted for its salt production from surrounding marshes.

The Finger Lakes of New York such as **Seneca Lake** and **Cayuga Lake,** are a series of slender north-south trending lakes produced by glaciers scouring the valleys as they moved southward. As the glaciers melted and receded they often left behind huge deposits of rocks, soil and other materials which formed drumlins. Several of these hills are visible on the photo-map north of the **Finger Lakes** area.

New York City

New York City, the business and financial heart of the country, is also the nation's largest city and leading port. At least six ships enter and leave the over 700 miles of waterfront every daylight hour.

New York City has more skycrapers than any other city in the world. Most of them are located on Manhattan Island. **Manhattan's** buildings represent one-fifth of all the office space in the United States.

The 840-acre **Central Park** was set aside in the 1850's in what was then the city's outskirts.

Over ten per cent of U.S. manufacturing is located in the New York City metropolitan area. The garment industry and other light industries are situated in New York City, while heavy industry such as petroleum refineries can be seen along the New Jersey shore in cities like **Newark** and **Jersey City.**

New York City is composed of five boroughs or counties: **Manhattan, Queens, Bronx, Brooklyn,** and **Richmond (Staten Island)**. Of these, only the Bronx is part of the New York State mainland.

Commercial airports in the New York metropolitan area include **John F. Kennedy International, LaGuardia,** and **Newark.** In terms of passengers handled, this is the busiest air center in the world.

Just north of the **Statue of Liberty** is **Ellis Island.** From 1892 to 1954, over 16 million immigrants were processed here before entering the United States.

The **Verrazano-Narrows Bridge** linking Brooklyn and Staten Island has a suspension span of 4,260 feet, the longest in the world.

Atlanta

Atlanta began in 1837 as a small railroad settlement called Terminus. Though General Sherman burned the city and tore up the railways in 1864, **Atlanta** re-emerged as the transportation center of the southeast —not only a rail center but one of the nation's leading focuses for highway and air traffic.

Atlanta's prominence as a transportation center is readily seen in this photo-map. **William B. Hartsfield International Airport** in the lower portion of the picture is the second busiest airport in the United States in terms of number of take-offs and landings. Auto expressways, railroad tracks, and parking lots are abundant. Between the gold-domed **State Capitol** and **Atlanta Stadium** is a large area devoted completely to traffic interchanges feeding into the downtown central business district.

The focus of transportation on **Atlanta** can partially be attributed to its strategic location at the southern tip of the Blue Ridge Mountains, in the populous section of Georgia known as the Piedmont plateau.

The outstanding industries of **Atlanta** are also transportation-oriented, especially the manufacturing of aircraft and automobiles. However, much of the burgeoning economy of the city is related to its increasing importance as the southeastern headquarters of many corporations and government agencies. **Atlanta** boasts that 430 of the 500 largest corporations in the United States maintain an operation within the city.

Atlanta's business district is situated around a junction of streets called Five Points. South of the business district is the **Atlanta Stadium,** with a seating capacity of 52,000.

With a metropolitan population of 1,390,000, **Atlanta** is growing rapidly, as evidenced by this photo-map. The formerly forested and cropped land on the city margins is rapidly being converted to urban uses.

Pepacton
Res.

Cayuga
Lake

Seneca
Lake

ITHACA

ALLEGHENY PLATEAU

BINGHAMTON

DANSVILLE

ELMIRA

NEW YORK
PENNSYLVANIA

WELLSVILLE

Susquehanna   River

SCRANTON

BLOSSBURG

WILKES BARRE

HAZELTON

WILLIAMSPORT

West   Branch of   the Susquehanna

MOUNTAINS

DANVILLE

SUNBURY

MOUNTAINS

GREAT   VALLEY

ALLEGHENY

GREAT

R

Juniata   River

Glendale
Lake

HARRISBURG

LANCASTER

ALTOONA

APPALACHIAN

Susquehanna

VALLEY

YORK

River

GREAT

VALLEY

GETTYSBURG

PENNSYLVANIA
MARYLAND

JOHNSTOWN

BALTIMORE

Many of New York's wines come from vineyards near the southern tips of the Finger Lakes. In this area, lake winds exert a modifying effect on the extremes of summer and winter weather experienced in the eastern part of the state. The favorable climate and soil make central New York well suited for fruit, vegetable, and dairy production.

In the middle of New Jersey, America's most densely populated state, is an almost unspoiled wilderness with 650,000 acres of pine and oak trees known as the **Pine Barrens.**

Atlantic City, New Jersey, and other resort cities were built on off-shore sand bars which have been formed by the movement of ocean currents and waves on the ocean bottom.

Eastern population clusters tend to be concentrated near the excellent harbors such as **New York City, Baltimore,** and **Philadelphia. Philadelphia,** the nation's capital from 1790 to 1800 is the largest fresh water port in the world. These three cities are part of a super-sized urban area called Megalopolis, which extends almost unbroken from Washington D.C. to Boston. The average population density for the region is 840 persons per square mile.

The Pennsylvania Dutch country is west of **Philadelphia** near the **Susquehanna River.** Curving strips of crops such as corn, hay and tobacco are contour-plowed to the shapes of the hills without the use of modern machinery.

In sharp contrast to Megalopolis, much of central Pennsylvania is as wild and unsettled as it was before the pioneers moved west. Rugged topography of the **Allegheny** and **Appalachian Mountains,** and poor soils hindered settlement and the construction of transportation arteries. The extensive dark areas on the photo-map are forests, and the grey, peppered areas are small farms. A light snowfall covers the landscape on the western edge of this photo-map around **Wellsville.**

The **Appalachian Mountains** apparently resulted from the folding of the earth's surface when the continents of North America and Africa were squeezed together about 200 million years ago.

PA.
MD.

CUMBERLAND

MARYLAND
WEST VIRGINIA

WEST VIRGINIA
VIRGINIA

MOUNTAINS

VALLEY

SHENANDOAH

BLUE RIDGE MOUNTAINS

PLATEAU

APPALACHIAN

MOUNTAINS

ALLEGHENY

W.VA.
VA.

SHENANDOAH MOUNTAINS

PIEDMONT

James River

LYNCHBURG

ROANOKE

Smith Mountain Lake

WASHINGTON D.C.

ALEXANDRIA

Potomac

Lake Anna

RICHM

John Kerr Res

BALTI

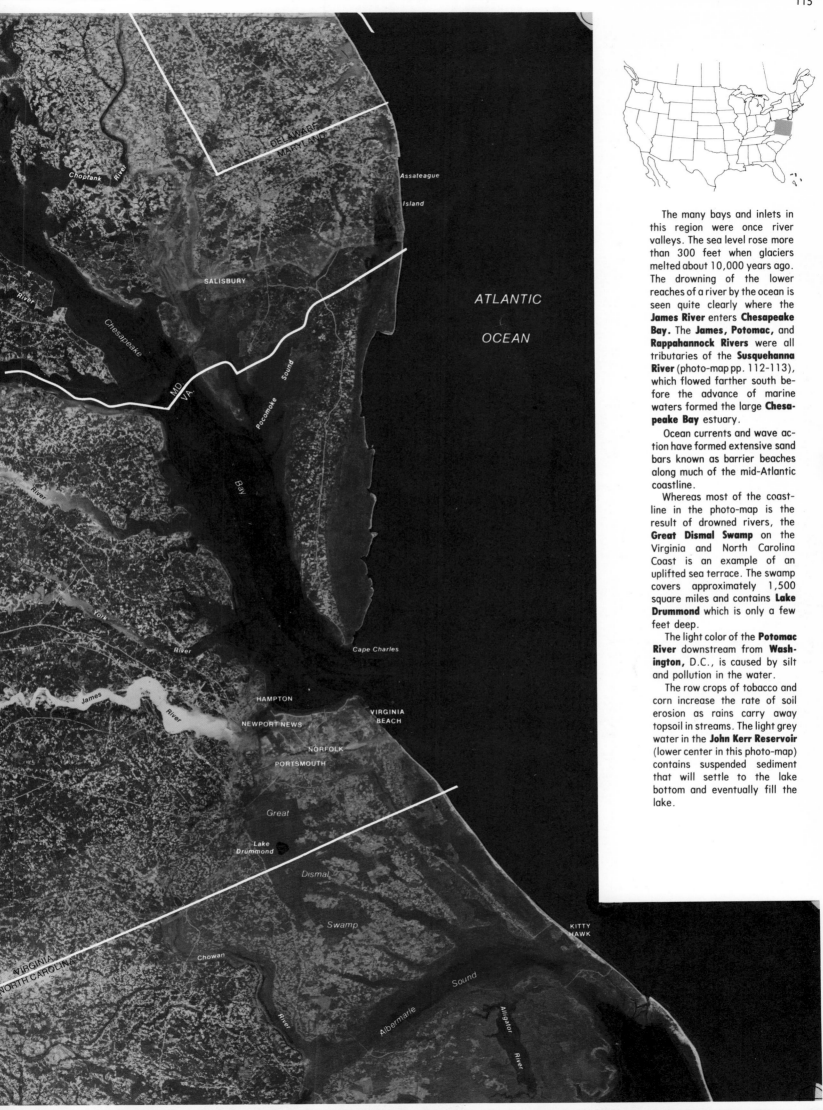

ATLANTIC

OCEAN

The many bays and inlets in this region were once river valleys. The sea level rose more than 300 feet when glaciers melted about 10,000 years ago. The drowning of the lower reaches of a river by the ocean is seen quite clearly where the **James River** enters **Chesapeake Bay.** The **James, Potomac,** and **Rappahannock Rivers** were all tributaries of the **Susquehanna River** (photo-map pp. 112-113), which flowed farther south before the advance of marine waters formed the large **Chesapeake Bay** estuary.

Ocean currents and wave action have formed extensive sand bars known as barrier beaches along much of the mid-Atlantic coastline.

Whereas most of the coastline in the photo-map is the result of drowned rivers, the **Great Dismal Swamp** on the Virginia and North Carolina Coast is an example of an uplifted sea terrace. The swamp covers approximately 1,500 square miles and contains **Lake Drummond** which is only a few feet deep.

The light color of the **Potomac River** downstream from **Washington,** D.C., is caused by silt and pollution in the water.

The row crops of tobacco and corn increase the rate of soil erosion as rains carry away topsoil in streams. The light grey water in the **John Kerr Reservoir** (lower center in this photo-map) contains suspended sediment that will settle to the lake bottom and eventually fill the lake.

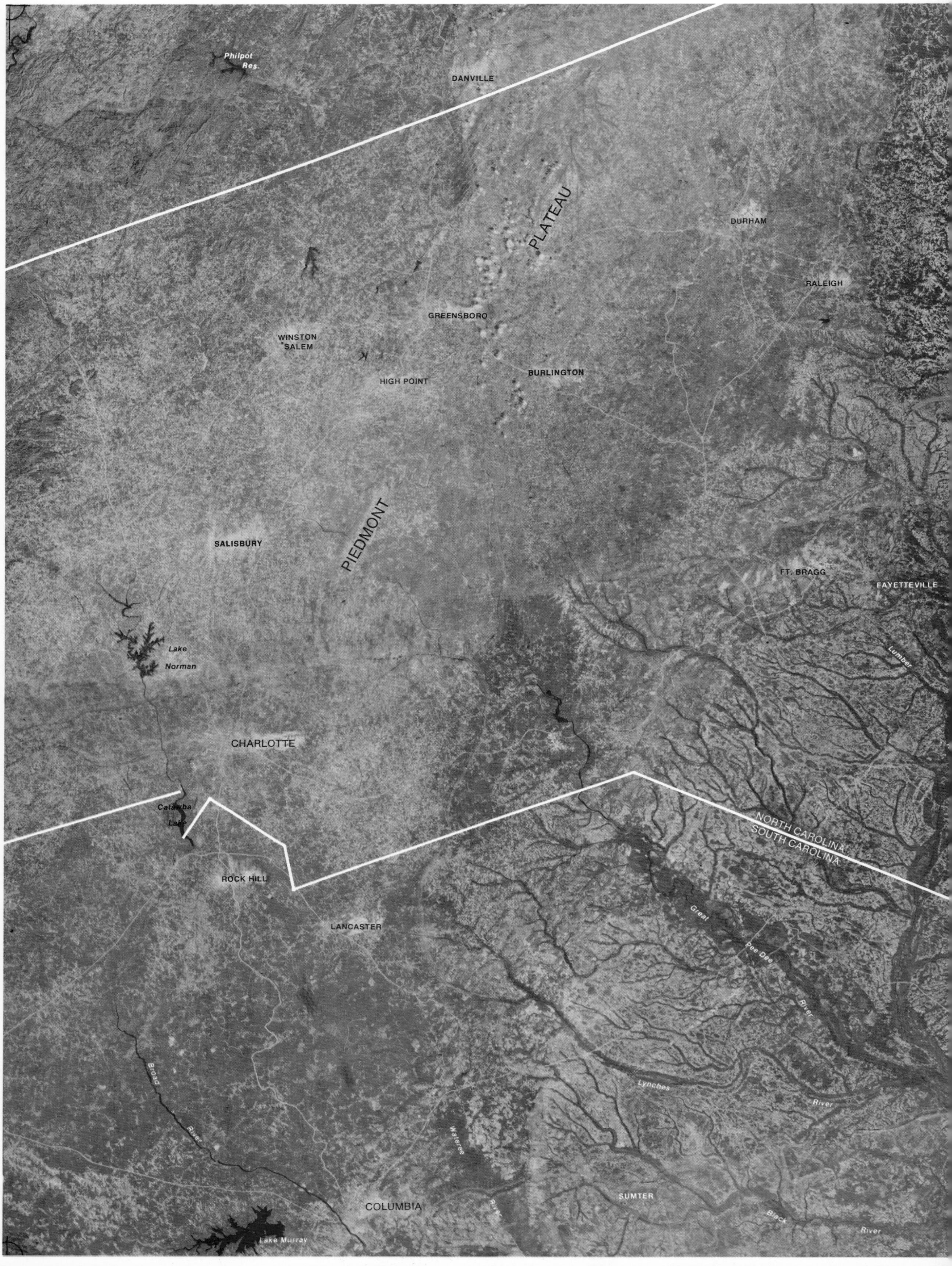

Philpot Res.

DANVILLE

PLATEAU

DURHAM

RALEIGH

GREENSBORO

WINSTON SALEM

BURLINGTON

HIGH POINT

PIEDMONT

SALISBURY

FT. BRAGG

FAYETTEVILLE

Lumber

Lake Norman

CHARLOTTE

Catawba Lake

NORTH CAROLINA
SOUTH CAROLINA

ROCK HILL

Great

Pee Dee

LANCASTER

River

Broad

Lynches

River

River

Wateree

COLUMBIA

SUMTER

Black

River

Lake Murray

117

Phelps Lake

Roanoke River

Intracoastal Waterway

Lake Mattamuskeet

Cape Hatteras

Pamlico Sound

Pungo River

Pamlico River

GREENVILLE

Pamlico

Raleigh Bay

Neuse River

GOLDSBORO

Intracoastal Waterway

Cape Lookout

JACKSONVILLE

Bay

Holly

Onslow

Shelter

Swamp

Cape Fear

River

WILMINGTON

ATLANTIC OCEAN

Cape Fear

Myrtle Beach

Offshore bars are prevalent along the coast in the northern portion of this photo-map. **Pamlico Sound** is surrounded by sand reefs with prominent projections like **Cape Hatteras** and **Cape Lookout.** Numerous estuaries, ancient sea-cliffs, and shoreline swamps characterize this area.

Cape Hatteras is noted for its dangerous storms which are caused in part by the meeting of the warm Gulf Stream winds with cooler land breezes. Some 30,000 acres of barrier reef south of the Cape have been declared a National Seashore in order to preserve the pristine and fragile environment.

Ships hug the Atlantic coast, transporting goods along the Eastern Seaboard. The Intracoastal Waterway, extending from Brownsville, Texas (photo-map pp. 82-83) north of Cape Cod (photo-map pg. 125), is a vital link in the nation's economy. In the northeastern portion of this photo-map, the waterway extends through channels dug in the salt marshes above **Cape Lookout** and northwest of **Lake Mattamuskeet.**

Inland, in the **Piedmont Plateau** region around **Winston-Salem** and **Durham** is the home of the tobacco industry.

Lumber and lumber by-products are an important economic factor in North Carolina. Pines thrive along the coastal plain. Lumber companies are purchasing land like that along the **Neuse River** and replanting depleted forests. The trees mature very rapidly in the humid subtropical climate.

SUMTER
NAT'L FOR

Santee Dam

Santee
River

Lake Marion

Lake
Moultrie

North

Fork

Copper
River

South

Fork

Edisto

River

Savannah River Plant
(A.E.C.)

Edisto

CHARLES

AUGUSTA

River

S.C.
GA.

Savannah

River

Parris Island

Ogeechee

BEAUFORT

Hilton
Head
Island

River

SAVANNAH

Canoochee

River

Occonee

River

Altamaha

River

Ocmulgee

River

BRUNSWICK

Satilla

River

WAYCROSS

Satilla

River

St. Mary's River

Atlantic Ocean

Winyah Bay

The dendritic drainage patterns seen in this photo-map typify the flat plains of the southern Atlantic Coast.

Carrying goods from Houston and New Orleans along the Atlantic Coast to northern ports and back, ships ply the **Intracoastal Waterway**—one of the busiest waterways in the world.

The Atomic Energy Commission's **Savannah River Plant** sprawls over an area of more than 100 square miles. The complex excavation, roads and buildings can be seen within the dark circular region that defines the plant. Radio-active waste that has accummulated over the years is stored here.

St. Marys River

Okefenokee Swamp

GA.
FLA.

Atlantic Ocean

JACKSONVILLE

St. Johns River

Intracoastal

Suwannee River

ST. AUGUSTINE

Waterway

Santa Fe River

Suwannee River

GAINESVILLE

Lake George

OF MEXICO

Limestone underlies much of central Florida. As rainwater seeps through the soil, it dissolves the limestone and produces sinkholes, which in turn fill with water. These sinkholes appear on the photo-map as circular lakes. Some are several miles wide.

The light dots visible along the the coast of the Cape are the individual launching pads of Cape Kennedy.

Lake Okeechobee is 40 miles long and over 25 miles wide but has a maximum depth of only 20 feet. The lake has no stream outlets. The water seeps through the soil to **The Everglades** in the south.

The Everglades is actually a wide river carrying water from **Lake Okeechobee** to the **Gulf of Mexico.** On this photo-map, surface water can be seen showing through the lush vegetation, primarily sawgrass, of **The Everglades.** These dashes of surface water indicate the general flow of the river. The photo-map also shows the agricultural activity and the urbanization from the north and the east that is threatening the delicate ecosystem of **The Everglades.**

The photo-image used for the Florida Keys is an example of infared imagery. The majority of images in the earth blue photo-maps of this atlas are from the red portion or band of the visible light spectrum.

PALM BEACH

FORT LAUDERDALE

MIAMI

Miami Canal

The Everglades

Keys

River

Caloosahatchee

FORT MEYERS

Charlotte

Pine Island

Cape Romano

Gulf of Mexico

Florida

KEY WEST

Portion of red band (MSS Band 5) image

KEY WEST

SAINT JOHN

Passamaquoddy Bay

Grand Manan

ACADIA NAT'L PARK

OROMOCTO

FREDERICTON

Oromocto Lake

River

St. John

ST. STEPHEN

CALAIS

St. Croix River

West Gand Lake

ELLSWORTH

BANGOR

Penobscot River

NEWPORT

HARTLAND

N.B.

MAINE

HOULTON

MILO

MILLINOCKET

MOUNTAINS

LONGFELLOW

CANADA

U.S.A.

Moosehead Lake

PRESQUE ISLE

Chesuncook Lake

CARIBOU

Chamberlain Lake

River

Allagash

U.S.A.

CANADA

MADAWASKA

St John River

EDMONSTON

MAINE

QUEBEC

ST GEORGE

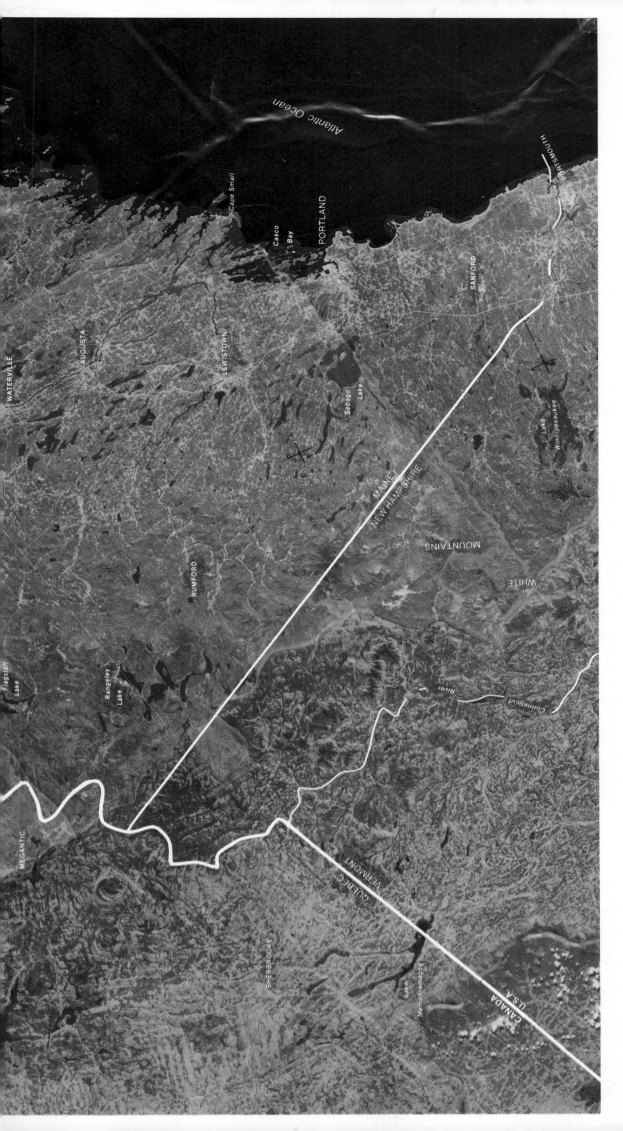

Atlantic Ocean

PORTSMOUTH

Cape Small

Casco Bay

PORTLAND

SANFORD

WATERVILLE

AUGUSTA

LEWISTOWN

Sebago Lake

Lake Winnipesaukee

MAINE

NEW HAMPSHIRE

MOUNTAINS

WHITE

RUMFORD

Flagstaff Lake

Rangeley Lake

Connecticut River

MEGANTIC

SHERBROOKE

QUEBEC

VERMONT

Lake Memphremagog

CANADA

U.S.A.

The rugged, indented shore-line of Maine is over 3,000 miles long. Numerous islands, deep bays and peninsulas formed as the eastern seacoast was submerged from the weight of ice-age glaciers and subsequently flooded by the rising sea level of post-glacial ages.

The range of the tides is high in this region, averaging twenty feet in places such as **Eastport,** Maine. The narrow channel opening into **Passamaquoddy Bay** contributes to the high tides there, where over 4 billion tons of water are exchanged daily. The latitude of this bay is 45 degrees north, halfway between the equator and the North Pole.

As glaciers melted, the ocean level rose and flooded the valleys of the New England coast. The resulting coves and harbors first served as homes for fishermen but now provide summer retreats and quaint towns for tourists.

Maine's inland topography also illustrates extensive glacial influence. Most of its 2,500 lakes were scoured out by glaciers. The circular dent in the landscape northeast of **Sherbrooke,** Quebec (about 2 inches on this photo-map) is not glacial, but probably of volcanic or meteoric origin.

Bangor, Maine was the world's leading lumber port in the 1820's. Called the Pine Tree State, Maine is still one of the top pulpwood producers in the country.

Coastal currents and shallow off-shore water depths provide ideal fishing waters. Maine's offshore waters produce over 75 per cent of the nation's lobsters and over 30 per cent of the soft shelled clams. Sardines are another leading industry. The state's total catch from the sea is valued at over $30 million annually.

The state of **Maine** is sparsely populated. Most of the 994,000 people live along the coast and over one-half the state's population is located in and around **Portland. Portland** was originally settled as a home for cod fishermen and today it is still a major U.S. fishing port. The city is the terminus for an oil pipeline from Montreal and is the second busiest oil shipment port on the Atlantic coast.

Boston

Boston was settled in 1630 on the bulging end of a narrow peninsula (Shawmut Peninsula) at the mouth of the **Charles River.** To provide room for expansion in the 19th and 20th centuries, landfill was used extensively. **Logan International Airport, South Boston** and the **Back Bay** are all on reclaimed land.

Boston developed in colonial times as a ship-building and fishing center. Today, with 120 miles of waterfront, it is a major New England seaport. Production of electronic equipment, machinery, shoes and clothes are an important part of the economy.

North of **Boston** is **Charleston.** The eastern end of **Charleston** is taken up by the **U.S. Navy Yard.** The U.S. Frigate <u>Constitution</u> (Old Ironsides) is on display here. Behind the Navy Yard is **Bunker Hill,** site of the famous 1775 revolutionary battle.

The 48-acre **Boston Commons** is the oldest public park in the United States. It was used as a cow pasture until 1830, and as a training field for British troops at the onset of the Revolutionary War. Today it is a public meeting place frequented by sidewalk orators.

On the left side of this photo-map, adjacent to the **Boston Commons** is the land-filled Back Bay area. The **Charles River** extended well into the present city before the 19th-century land reclamation project was begun. The Charles River Dam blocks the flow of ocean tides and regulates the water level in the estuary.

Cambridge is the home of several well-known universities including **M.I.T.,** Harvard and Radcliff.

In contrast to the predominantly rocky coast of Maine (see photo-map pp. 122-123) the Atlantic shoreline in this photo-map is characterized by abundant sandy beaches. The shoreline is the result of submergence of the mainland, but the rocks along the shores in this photo-map have been less resistant to wave erosion than the coastal rocks to the north. **Plum Island,** south of **Newburyport,** and the well-known **Cape Cod** are popular New England beaches.

Cape Cod is constantly changing in size and shape. Ocean currents slowly deposit and remove sand from the shores. Storms may produce drastic shoreline changes very rapidly. To preserve the natural beauty, nearly 27,000 acres of **Cape Cod** have been set aside as the Cape Cod National Seashore.

The Pilgrims landed near **Provincetown** in 1620 and then sailed across **Cape Cod Bay** to **Plymouth,** where they established the first permanent settlement in America north of Virginia.

Martha's Vineyard and **Nantucket Island** were once great whaling ports. Privateers stayed in hiding on **Block Island** during colonial times. Today these islands are vacation meccas for northeast metropolitan areas.

The 175-mile-long **Cape Cod Canal** was built to enable sailors to avoid submerged sandbars and other hazards of navigating around **Cape Cod.** The canal, which connects **Buzzards Bay** to **Cape Cod Bay,** is now part of the Intracoastal Waterway that stretches from Maine to Texas.

Pawtucket, Rhode Island is the birthplace of America's cotton textile industry. Here, in 1793, Samuel Slater built the first machine-equipped textile mill using **Blackstone River** water for power.

Concord, New Hampshire, on the **Merrimack River,** is the state's capital. The city is also known for the white granite mined in nearby quarries. New Hampshire is nick-named The Granite State because of its extensive granite works.

Glaciers left southeastern Massachusetts a land of marshes and ponds. The sandy soils of the swamps and bogs around **Cape Cod** are ideal for raising cranberries, of which the state is one of the leading producers in the Nation.

BARROW

Teshekp L.

BROOKS

KOTZEBUE

Kotzebue Sound

Strait

Bering

Seward

Peninsula

ARCTIC

NOME

St. Lawrence Island

Norton

Sound

Yukon

River

Yukon

MOUNTAINS

River

KUSKOKWIM

Kuskokwim

River

BETHEL

RANGE

Lliamna Lake

Cook Inlet

ALASKA

Bristol

Bay

KATMAI

NATIONAL

MONUMENT

KODIAK

Kodiak

Island

Peninsula

Alaska

DUTCH HARBOR

Islands

Aleutian

The most productive agricultural areas in Alaska are the **Matanuska Valley** north of **Anchorage,** the **Tanana Valley** near **Fairbanks,** and the **Kenai Peninsula.** The growing season is a short 100 days, but because the summer days are so long, vegetables and berries grow to huge proportions without losing flavor.

The southeastern portion of Alaska which extends 400 miles along the Pacific coast bordering Canada is called the **Alaskan Panhandle.** The Panhandle is as large as New England and is a major fishing and lumbering region.

The northern panhandle is a land of Glaciers. Near the Juneau Airport, **Mendenhall Glacier** descends to within 60 feet of sea level. Northwest of **Juneau** is **Glacier Bay National Monument** encompassing 4,380 square miles. This is the largest national monument in the United States. **Malaspina Glacier** on the Gulf of Alaska is larger than the state of Rhode Island.

A spectacular example of the unique ability of photo-maps to show shadows is the shadow cast by **Mount McKinley** (just above the "T" in Mount). At 20,320 feet, Mount McKinley is the highest peak in North America, towering thousands of feet above its neighboring peaks in the **Alaska Range.**

In 1968 immense oil reserves were discovered under the permafrost on Alaska's North Slope. To convey this oil to a shipping port, an 800-mile-long pipeline is being built. The controversial pipeline will begin at **Prudhoe Bay** on the **Arctic Ocean** and transverse Alaska via **Fairbanks** to **Valdez** in the south. Ecologists are concerned that the pipeline could permanently damage the delicate Tundra region and alter the migration habits of the large caribou herds of the north. The pipeline is shown graphically by a dashed line along its route.

Alaska, with 586,400 square miles, is larger than the combined areas of Texas, California, and Montana. The Alaskan coastline, including islands, is 26,000 miles long. While first in land area, Alaska ranks last in population with 300,000 people.

The **Katmai National Monument** on the **Alaskan Peninsula** is one of the areas of volcanic activity in the state. The world's longest chain of active volcanoes extends throughout the **Aleutian Islands.**